GCSE AQA

Combined Science
Physics

Foundation Level

Physics is a big part of GCSE Combined Science... and it's not easy. But CGP are on the case — this brilliant book has it covered, from facts and theory to practical skills.

We've also included plenty of exam-style practice for every topic *and* a full set of Physics practice papers so that you can put your new-found knowledge to the test.

How to access your free Online Edition

This book includes a free Online Edition to read on your PC, Mac or tablet.
You'll just need to go to **cgpbooks.co.uk/extras** and enter this code:

3467 8133 6377 3462

By the way, this code only works for one person. If somebody else has used this book before you, they might have already claimed the Online Edition.

Complete
Revision & Practice

Everything you need to pass the exams!

Contents

Throughout this book you'll see grade stamps like these:

These grade stamps help to show how difficult the questions are.

Remember — to get a top grade you need to be able to answer **all** the questions, not just the hardest ones.

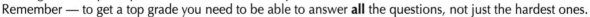

In the real exams, some questions test how well you can structure an answer (as well as your scientific knowledge). In this book, we've marked these questions with an asterisk (*).

Published by CGP

From original material by Richard Parsons.

Editors: Sarah Armstrong, Luke Bennett, Sharon Keeley-Holden, Stephen Walters and Sarah Williams.

Contributor: Paddy Gannon.

With thanks to Mark Edwards, Duncan Lindsay and Karen Wells for the proofreading.

With thanks to Emily Smith for the copyright research.

Stopping distances data on pages 105 and 164 from The Highway Code.
Contains public sector information licensed under the Open Government Licence v3.0.
http://www.nationalarchives.gov.uk/doc/open-government-licence/version/3/

ISBN: 978 1 78908 004 9

Printed by Elanders Ltd, Newcastle upon Tyne.
Clipart from Corel®

What to Expect in the Exams

It's nearly time to get cracking with your revision and exam practice. First, here's a handy guide to what you'll have to face in the exams — and the special features of this book that we've included especially to help you. You're welcome.

1. Topics are Covered in Different Papers

For GCSE Combined Science, you'll sit six exam papers at the end of your course, including two physics exams.

You're expected to know the basic concepts of physics in both physics papers.

Paper	Time	No. of marks	Topics Assessed
Physics 1	1 hr 15 mins	70	1, 2, 3 and 4
Physics 2	1 hr 15 mins	70	5, 6 and 7

2. There are Different Question Types

In each exam, you'll be expected to answer a mixture of multiple choice questions, structured questions, questions that have short, closed answers, as well as open response questions.

For some open response questions, you'll be marked on the overall quality of your answer, not just its scientific content. So...

Fortunately, we've included loads of questions in this book, as well as a set of practice papers to give you the best possible preparation for the exams.

Always make sure:
- You answer the question fully.
- You include detailed, relevant information.
- Your answer is clear and has a logical structure.

In the exam practice questions, we've marked these questions with an asterisk (*).

3. You'll be Tested on Your Maths...

At least 30% of the total marks in the physics exams in GCSE Combined Science will come from questions that test your maths skills. For these questions, always remember to:

Look out for these worked examples in this book — they show you maths skills you'll need in the exam.

- Show your working — you could get marks for this, even if your final answer's wrong.
- Check that the units of your answer are the same as the ones they asked for in the question.
- Make sure your answer is given to an appropriate number of significant figures.

4. ...and on Your Practical Skills

Whenever one of the required practicals crops up in this book, it's marked up with stamps like these...

...and there's a whole section on Practical Skills on pages 132-136.

- GCSE Combined Science contains 21 required practicals that you'll do during the course. The 8 physics practicals are covered in this book. You can be asked about these, and the practical skills involved in them, in the exams.
- At least 15% of the total marks will be for questions that test your understanding of the practical activities and practical skills.
- For example, you might be asked to comment on the design of an experiment (the apparatus and method), make predictions, analyse or interpret results... Pretty much anything to do with planning and carrying out the investigations.

5. You'll need to know about Working Scientifically

Working Scientifically is all about how science is applied in the outside world by real scientists.

For example, you might be asked about ways that scientists communicate an idea to get their point across without being biased, or about the limitations of a scientific theory.

Working Scientifically is covered on pages 2-17.

You need to think about the situation that you've been given and use all your scientific savvy to answer the question. Always read the question and any data you've been given really carefully before you start writing your answer.

The Scientific Method

This section <u>isn't</u> about how to 'do' science — but it does show you the way <u>most scientists</u> work.

Scientists Make an Observation

1) Scientists <u>observe</u> (look at) something they don't understand, e.g. visible light.

2) They come up with a <u>possible explanation</u> for what they've observed.

3) This explanation is called a <u>hypothesis</u>.

They Test Their Hypothesis

1) Next, they test whether the hypothesis is <u>right or not</u>.

2) They do this by making a <u>prediction</u> — a statement based on the hypothesis that can be tested.

3) They then <u>test</u> this prediction by carrying out <u>experiments</u>.

4) If their prediction is <u>right</u>, this is <u>evidence</u> that their <u>hypothesis might be right</u> too.

About 100 years ago, scientists hypothesised that atoms looked like this.

Other Scientists Test the Hypothesis too

1) Other scientists <u>check</u> the evidence — for example, they check that the experiment was carried out in a <u>sensible</u> way. This is called <u>peer-review</u>.

2) Scientists then <u>share their results</u>, e.g. in scientific papers.

3) Other scientists carry out <u>more experiments</u> to test the hypothesis.

4) Sometimes these scientists will find <u>more evidence</u> that the <u>hypothesis is right</u>.

5) Sometimes they'll find <u>evidence</u> that shows the <u>hypothesis is wrong</u>.

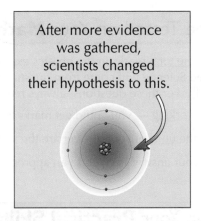

After more evidence was gathered, scientists changed their hypothesis to this.

The Hypothesis is Accepted or Rejected

1) If <u>all the evidence</u> that's been found <u>supports</u> the <u>hypothesis</u>, it becomes an <u>accepted theory</u> and goes into <u>textbooks</u> for people to learn.

2) If the <u>evidence</u> shows that the hypothesis is <u>wrong</u>, scientists must:
   - <u>Change the hypothesis</u>, or
   - Come up with a <u>new hypothesis</u>.

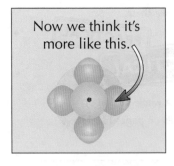

Now we think it's more like this.

Observe, hypothesise, test, repeat...

The <u>scientific method</u> has been <u>developed</u> over time. Aristotle (a Greek philosopher) was the first person to realise that theories need to be based on <u>observations</u>. Muslim scholars then introduced the ideas of creating a <u>hypothesis</u>, <u>testing</u> it, and <u>repeating</u> work to check results.

Models and Communication

Once scientists have made a <u>new discovery</u>, they <u>don't</u> just keep it to themselves. Oh no. Time to learn about how scientific discoveries are <u>communicated</u>, and the <u>models</u> that are used to represent theories.

Theories Can Involve **Different Types** of **Models**

1) A <u>model</u> is a <u>simple way</u> of <u>describing</u> or <u>showing</u> what's going on in <u>real life</u>.
2) Models can be used to <u>explain ideas</u> and <u>make predictions</u>. For example:

> The <u>particle model</u> gives a simple <u>picture</u> of what matter is made of.
> It can be used to explain the behaviour of gases. (See p.64 for more.)

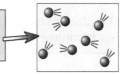

3) All models have <u>limits</u> — a single model <u>can't explain</u> everything about an idea.

It's Important to **Tell People** About Scientific Discoveries

1) Scientific discoveries can make a big difference to <u>people's lives</u>.
2) So scientists need to <u>tell the world</u> about their discoveries.
3) They might need to tell people to <u>change their habits</u>, e.g. use less fossil fuel to help stop climate change.
4) Alternatively, the discoveries might provide <u>ideas</u> that could be developed into new <u>technologies</u>.

> <u>Radioactive materials</u> are used widely in <u>medicine</u> for <u>imaging</u> and <u>treatment</u>.
> Information about these materials needs to be communicated to <u>doctors</u> so they can <u>make use</u> of them, and to <u>patients</u> so they can make <u>informed decisions</u> about their <u>treatment</u>.

Scientific **Evidence** can be **Presented** in a **Biased Way**

1) <u>Reports</u> about scientific discoveries in the <u>media</u> (e.g. newspapers or television) can be <u>misleading</u>.
2) The data might be <u>presented</u> in a way that's <u>not quite right</u> — or it might be <u>oversimplified</u>.
3) This means that people may not <u>properly understand</u> what the scientists found out.
4) People who want to make a point can also sometimes <u>present data</u> in a <u>biased way</u> (in a way that's <u>unfair</u> or <u>ignores</u> one side of the argument). For example:

- A <u>scientist</u> may talk a lot about <u>one particular relationship</u> in the data (and not mention others).
- A <u>newspaper article</u> might describe data <u>supporting</u> an idea without giving any evidence <u>against</u> it.

Companies can present biased data to help sell products...

Sometimes a company may only want you to see half of the story so they present the data in a <u>biased way</u>. For example, a pharmaceutical company may want to encourage you to buy their drugs by telling you about all the <u>positives</u>, but not report the results of any <u>unfavourable studies</u>.

Issues Created by Science

Science has helped us make progress in loads of areas, from advances in medicine to space travel. But science still has its issues. And it can't answer everything, as you're about to find out.

Scientific Developments are Great, but they can Raise Issues

1) Scientific developments include new technologies and new advice.
2) These developments can create issues. For example:

Economic (money) issues: Society can't always afford to do things scientists recommend, like spend money on green energy sources.

Social (people) issues: Decisions based on scientific evidence affect people — e.g. should alcohol be banned (to prevent health problems)?

Personal issues: Some decisions will affect individuals — e.g. people may be upset if a wind farm is built next to their house.

Environmental issues: Human activity often affects the environment — e.g. clearing forests to grow biofuels can have a negative impact on the local environment.

Science Can't Answer Every Question — Especially Ethical Ones

1) At the moment scientists don't agree on some things — like what the universe is made of.
2) This is because there isn't enough data to support the scientists' hypotheses.
3) But eventually, we probably will be able to answer these questions once and for all.
4) Experiments can't tell us whether something is ethically right or wrong.
5) The best we can do is make a decision that most people are more or less happy to live by.

Think about new drugs which can be taken to boost your 'brain power'.

- Some people think they're good as they could improve concentration or memory. New drugs could let people think in ways beyond the powers of normal brains.

- Other people say they're bad — they could give some people an unfair advantage in exams. And people might be pressured into taking them so that they could work more effectively, and for longer hours.

There are often issues with new scientific developments...

The trouble is, there's often no clear right answer where these issues are concerned. Different people have different views, depending on their priorities. These issues are full of grey areas.

Risk

Scientific discoveries are often great, but they can prove risky. With dangers all around, you've got to be aware of hazards — this includes how likely they are to cause harm and how serious the effects may be.

Nothing is Completely **Risk-Free**

1) A hazard is something that could cause harm.

2) All hazards have a risk attached to them — this is the chance that the hazard will cause harm.

3) New technology can bring new risks. E.g. scientists are creating technology to capture and store carbon dioxide. But if the carbon dioxide leaked out it could damage soil or water supplies. These risks need to be considered alongside the benefits of the technology, e.g. lower greenhouse gas emissions.

4) To make a decision about activities that involve hazards, we need to think about:
   - the chance of the hazard causing harm,
   - how bad the outcome (consequences) would be if it did.

People Make Their **Own Decisions** About Risk

1) Not all risks have the same consequences. For example, if you chop veg with a sharp knife you risk cutting your finger, but if you go scuba-diving you risk death.

2) Most people are happier to accept a risk if the consequences don't last long and aren't serious.

3) People tend to think familiar activities are low-risk. They tend to think unfamiliar activities are high-risk. But this isn't always true. For example:

   - Cycling on roads is often high-risk. But it's a familiar activity, so many people are happy to do it.
   - Air travel is actually pretty safe, but a lot of people think it is high-risk.

4) The best way to estimate the size of a risk is to look at data. E.g. you could estimate the risk of a driver crashing by recording how many people in a group of 100 000 drivers crashed their cars over a year.

The pros and cons of new technology must be weighed up...

The world's a dangerous place and it's impossible to rule out the chance of an accident altogether. But if you can recognise hazards and take steps to reduce the risks, you're more likely to stay safe.

Designing Investigations

Dig out your lab coat and dust down your safety goggles... it's <u>investigation time</u>.

Evidence Can **Support** or **Disprove** a **Hypothesis**

1) Scientists <u>observe</u> things and come up with <u>hypotheses</u> to explain them (see p.2).
You need to be able to do the same. For example:

> <u>Observation</u>: People have big feet and spots. <u>Hypothesis</u>: Having big feet causes spots.

2) To <u>find out</u> if your hypothesis is <u>right</u>, you need to do an <u>investigation</u> to gather evidence.

3) To do this, you need to use your hypothesis to make a <u>prediction</u> — something you think <u>will happen</u> that you can <u>test</u>. E.g. people who have bigger feet will have more spots.

4) Investigations are used to see if there are <u>patterns</u> or <u>relationships</u> between <u>two variables</u> (see below).

Make an Investigation a **Fair Test** By **Controlling the Variables**

1) In a lab experiment you usually <u>change one variable</u> and <u>measure</u> how it affects <u>another variable</u>.

> <u>EXAMPLE:</u> You could find how <u>current</u> through a circuit component affects the <u>potential difference</u> across the component by measuring the <u>potential difference</u> at different currents.

2) To make it a fair test, <u>everything else</u> that could affect the results should <u>stay the same</u>
— otherwise you can't tell if the thing you're changing is causing the results or not.

3) The variable you <u>CHANGE</u> is called the <u>INDEPENDENT</u> variable.

4) The variable you <u>MEASURE</u> when you change the independent variable is the <u>DEPENDENT</u> variable.

5) The variables that you <u>KEEP THE SAME</u> are called <u>CONTROL</u> variables.

> <u>EXAMPLE CONTINUED:</u>
> * The <u>independent variable</u> is the <u>current</u>.
> * The <u>dependent variable</u> is the <u>potential difference</u>.
> * The <u>control variables</u> include the <u>temperature</u> of the component, the <u>pd</u> of the power supply, etc.

6) Because you can't always control all the variables, you often need to use a <u>control experiment</u>.

7) This is an experiment that's kept under the <u>same conditions</u> as the rest of the investigation, but <u>doesn't</u> have anything <u>done</u> to it. This is so that you can see what happens when you don't change anything at all.

Evidence Needs to be **Repeatable, Reproducible** and **Valid**

1) <u>Repeatable</u> means that if the <u>same person</u> does the experiment again, they'll get <u>similar results</u>.
To check your results are repeatable, <u>repeat</u> the readings <u>at least three times</u>.
Then check the repeat results are all similar.

2) <u>Reproducible</u> means that if <u>someone else</u> does the experiment, the results will still be <u>similar</u>.
To make sure your results are reproducible, get <u>another person</u> to do the experiment too.

3) <u>Valid results</u> come from experiments that were designed to be a <u>fair test</u>.
They're also repeatable and reproducible.

If data is repeatable and reproducible, scientists are more likely to trust it.

Designing Investigations

The **Bigger** the **Sample Size** the **Better**

1) Sample size is <u>how many things you test</u> in an investigation, e.g. 500 people or 20 types of metal.

2) The <u>bigger</u> the sample size the <u>better</u> — to <u>reduce</u> the chance of any <u>weird results</u>.

3) But scientists have to be <u>realistic</u> when choosing how big their sample should be. For example:

> If you were studying the effects of <u>living</u> near a <u>nuclear power plant</u>, it'd be great to study <u>everyone</u> who lived near a nuclear power plant (a huge sample), but it'd take ages and cost a bomb.

4) When you choose a sample, you need to make sure you've got a <u>range</u> of different people.

5) For example, both <u>men</u> and <u>women</u> with a range of <u>different ages</u>.

Your **Equipment** has to be **Right for the Job**

1) The measuring equipment you use has to be <u>sensitive enough</u> to measure the changes you're looking for. E.g. if you need to measure out 11 cm³ of a liquid, use a <u>measuring cylinder</u> that can measure to 1 cm³ — not 5 or 10 cm³.

2) The <u>smallest change</u> a measuring instrument can <u>detect</u> is called its <u>resolution</u>. E.g. some mass balances have a resolution of 1 g, some have a resolution of 0.1 g, and some are even more sensitive.

3) You also need to <u>set up the equipment properly</u>. For example, make sure your <u>mass balance</u> is set to <u>zero</u> before you start weighing things.

Your Data Should be **Accurate** and **Precise**

1) <u>Accurate results</u> are results that are <u>really close</u> to the <u>true answer</u>.

2) The accuracy of your results usually depends on your <u>method</u>. You need to make sure you're measuring the <u>right thing</u>.

3) You also need to make sure you <u>don't miss anything</u> that should be included in the measurements. For example:

> Estimating the <u>volume</u> of an irregularly shaped solid by <u>measuring the sides</u> isn't very accurate because this will not take into account any gaps in the object. It's <u>more accurate</u> to measure the volume using a <u>eureka can</u> (see p.66).

4) <u>Precise results</u> are ones where the data is <u>all really close</u> to the <u>mean</u> (average) of your repeated results.

Data set 1 is more <u>precise</u> than data set 2.

Repeat	Data set 1	Data set 2
1	12	11
2	14	17
3	13	14
Mean	<u>13</u>	<u>14</u>

Designing Investigations

You Need to Look out for **Errors** and **Anomalous Results**

1) The results of your experiment will always <u>vary a bit</u> because of <u>random errors</u> — for example, mistakes you might make while <u>measuring</u>.

2) You can <u>reduce</u> the effect of random errors by taking <u>repeat readings</u> and finding the <u>mean</u>. This will make your results <u>more precise</u>.

3) If a measurement is wrong by the <u>same amount every time</u>, it's called a <u>systematic error</u>. For example:

> If you measure from the <u>very end</u> of your <u>ruler</u> instead of from the <u>0 cm mark</u> every time, <u>all</u> your measurements would be a bit <u>small</u>.
>
> Always measure from here...
>
> ...not here.

4) If you know you've made a systematic error, you might be able to <u>correct it</u>. For example, by adding a bit on to all your measurements.

5) Sometimes you get a result that <u>doesn't fit in</u> with the rest. This is called an <u>anomalous result</u>.

6) You should try to <u>work out what happened</u>. If you do (e.g. you find out you measured something wrong) you can <u>ignore</u> it when processing your results (see next page).

Investigations Can Have **Hazards**

1) Hazards from science experiments include things like:

> - <u>Lasers</u>, e.g. if a laser is directed into the eye, this can cause blindness.
> - <u>Gamma radiation</u>, e.g. gamma-emitting radioactive sources can cause cancer.
> - <u>Fire</u>, e.g. an unattended Bunsen burner is a fire hazard.
> - <u>Electricity</u>, e.g. faulty electrical equipment could give you a shock.

2) When you <u>plan</u> an investigation you need to make sure that it's <u>safe</u>.

3) You should <u>identify</u> all the hazards that you might come across.

4) Then you should think of ways of <u>reducing the risks</u>. For example:

There's more on safety in experiments on page 136.

> - If you're working with <u>springs</u>, always wear safety goggles. This will reduce the risk of the spring hitting your eye if the spring snaps.
> - If you're using a <u>Bunsen burner</u>, stand it on a heat proof mat to reduce the risk of starting a fire.

Designing an investigation is an involved process...

<u>Collecting data</u> is what investigations are all about. Designing a good investigation is really important to make sure that any data collected is <u>accurate</u>, <u>precise</u>, <u>repeatable</u> and <u>reproducible</u>.

Processing Data

Processing your data means doing some <u>calculations</u> with it to make it <u>more useful</u>.

You Can Find the **Mean**, the **Range**, the **Median** or the **Mode**

1) When you've done repeats of an experiment you should always calculate the <u>mean</u> (a type of average).

2) You might also need to calculate the <u>range</u> (how spread out the data is).

 **The results of an experiment show the extension of a spring when a force is applied.**
Calculate the mean and range of the extension.

Repeat (cm)					Mean (cm)	Range (cm)
1	**2**	**3**	**4**	**5**		
18	26	22	26	28	(18 + 26 + 22 + 26 + 28) ÷ 5 = 24	28 − 18 = 26

3) To find the <u>median</u>, put all your data in <u>order</u> from smallest to largest. The median is the <u>middle value</u>.

4) The number that appears <u>most often</u> is the <u>mode</u>.

If you have an even number of values, the median is halfway between the middle two values.

E.g. if you have the data set: 1 2 1 1 3 4 2

The <u>median</u> is: 1 1 1 <u>2</u> 2 3 4. The <u>mode</u> is <u>1</u> because 1 appears most often.

5) When calculating any of these values, always <u>ignore</u> any <u>anomalous results</u>.

Round to the **Lowest Number** of **Significant Figures**

1) The <u>first significant figure</u> of a number is the first digit that's <u>not zero</u>.

2) The second and third significant figures come <u>straight after</u> (even if they're zeros).

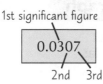

1st significant figure

0.0307

2nd   3rd

3) In <u>any</u> calculation, you should round the answer to the <u>lowest number of significant figures</u> (s.f.) given.

4) If your calculation has more than one step, <u>only</u> round the <u>final</u> answer.

EXAMPLE: **The mass of a solid is 0.24 g and its volume is 0.715 cm³.**
Calculate the density of the solid.

Density = 0.24 g ÷ 0.715 cm³ = 0.33566... = 0.34 g/cm³ (2 s.f.)

2 s.f.   3 s.f.   Final answer should be rounded to 2 s.f.

 ## Don't forget your calculator...

In the exam, you might be told to give an answer to a certain number of <u>significant figures</u>. Make sure you do this or you won't get all the marks. <u>Always write down your working too</u>.

Presenting Data

Once you've processed your data, e.g. by calculating the mean, you can present your results in a nice <u>chart</u> or <u>graph</u>. This will help you to <u>spot any patterns</u> in your data.

Data Needs to be Organised

1) <u>Tables</u> are useful for <u>organising data</u>.
2) When you draw a table <u>use a ruler</u>.
3) Make sure <u>each column</u> has a <u>heading</u> (including the <u>units</u>).

Spring	Repeat 1 (mm)	Repeat 2 (mm)
A	28	37
B	47	51

If Your Data Comes in Categories, Present It in a Bar Chart

If the independent variable comes in <u>clear categories</u> (e.g. solid, liquid, gas) or can be <u>counted exactly</u> (e.g. number of protons) you should use a <u>bar chart</u> to display the data. Here's what to do:

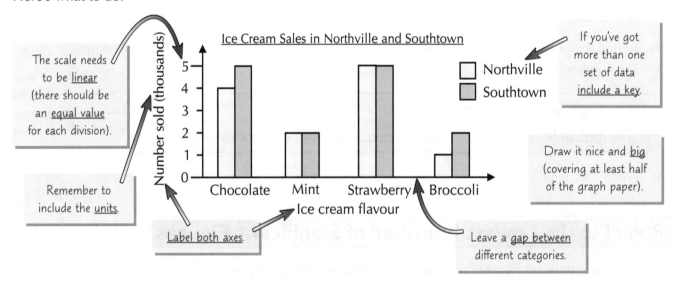

The scale needs to be <u>linear</u> (there should be an <u>equal value</u> for each division).

Remember to include the <u>units</u>.

If you've got more than one set of data <u>include a key</u>.

Draw it nice and <u>big</u> (covering at least half of the graph paper).

<u>Label both axes</u>.

Leave a <u>gap between</u> different categories.

If Your Data is Continuous, Plot a Graph

If both variables can have any value <u>within a range</u> (e.g. length, volume) use a <u>graph</u> to display the data:

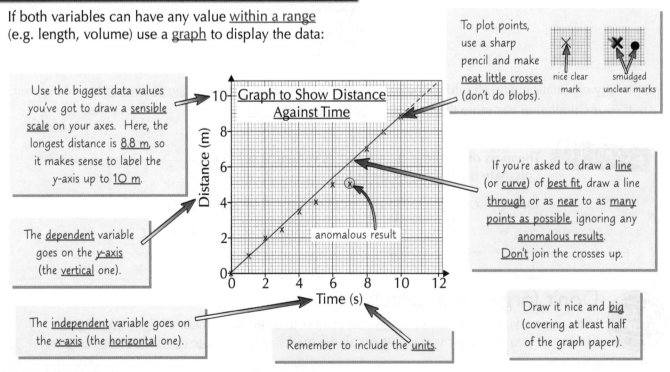

Use the biggest data values you've got to draw a <u>sensible scale</u> on your axes. Here, the longest distance is <u>8.8 m</u>, so it makes sense to label the y-axis up to <u>10 m</u>.

The <u>dependent</u> variable goes on the <u>y-axis</u> (the <u>vertical</u> one).

The <u>independent</u> variable goes on the <u>x-axis</u> (the <u>horizontal</u> one).

To plot points, use a sharp pencil and make <u>neat little crosses</u> (don't do blobs).

nice clear mark

smudged unclear marks

If you're asked to draw a <u>line</u> (or <u>curve</u>) of <u>best fit</u>, draw a line <u>through</u> or as <u>near</u> to as <u>many points as possible</u>, ignoring any <u>anomalous results</u>. <u>Don't</u> join the crosses up.

Remember to include the <u>units</u>.

Draw it nice and <u>big</u> (covering at least half of the graph paper).

More on Graphs

Graph's aren't just fun to plot, they're also really useful for showing <u>trends</u> in your data.

Graphs Can Give You a Lot of Information About Your Data

1) This is the <u>formula</u> you need to calculate the <u>gradient</u> (slope) of a graph:

$$\text{gradient} = \frac{\text{change in } y}{\text{change in } x}$$

2) <u>Gradient</u> tells you how quickly the <u>dependent variable</u> changes as you change the <u>independent variable</u>.

EXAMPLE:

This graph shows the distance travelled by a vehicle against time. Calculate the speed of the vehicle.

1) To calculate the <u>gradient</u>, pick <u>two points</u> on the line that are easy to read. They should also be a <u>good distance</u> apart.

2) Draw a line <u>down</u> from the higher point. Then draw a line <u>across</u> from the other, to make a <u>triangle</u>.

3) The line drawn <u>down the side</u> of the triangle is the <u>change in y</u>. The line <u>across the bottom</u> is the <u>change in x</u>.

4) Read the x and y values of the points <u>off the graph</u> and work out the change in y and the change in x:

Change in y = 6.8 − 2.0 = 4.8 m   Change in x = 5.2 − 1.6 = 3.6 s

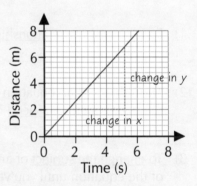

5) Then put these numbers in the formula above to find the rate of the reaction:

$$\text{Rate} = \text{gradient} = \frac{\text{change in } y}{\text{change in } x} = \frac{4.8 \text{ m}}{3.6 \text{ s}} = 1.3 \text{ m/s}$$

The units are (units of y)/(units of x). m/s can also be written as ms⁻¹.

Graphs Show the Relationship Between Two Variables

1) You can get <u>three</u> types of <u>correlation</u> (relationship) between variables:

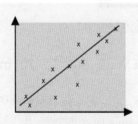

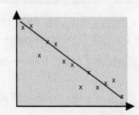

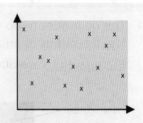

<u>Positive correlation:</u>
as one variable <u>increases</u> the other <u>increases</u>.

<u>Inverse (negative) correlation:</u>
as one variable <u>increases</u> the other <u>decreases</u>.

<u>No correlation:</u>
<u>no relationship</u> between the two variables.

2) A correlation <u>doesn't mean</u> the change in one variable is <u>causing</u> the change in the other (see page 15).

Equations and Units

Graphs and maths skills are all very well, but the numbers don't mean much if you can't get the <u>units</u> right.

S.I. Units Are Used All Round the World

1) All scientists use the same <u>units</u> to measure their data.

2) These are <u>standard units</u>, called S.I. units.

3) Here are some S.I. units you might see:

Quantity	S.I. Base Unit
mass	kilogram, kg
length	metre, m
time	second, s
temperature	kelvin, K

You Can **Rearrange** Equations

1) Equations show <u>relationships</u> between <u>variables</u>. For example, $\text{speed} = \dfrac{\text{distance}}{\text{time}}$.

2) The <u>subject</u> of an equation is the variable <u>by itself</u> on one side of the equals sign. So <u>speed</u> is the <u>subject</u> in the equation above.

3) To <u>change</u> the <u>subject</u> of an equation do the same thing to <u>both sides</u> of the equation until you've got the subject you <u>want</u>.

E.g. you can make <u>distance</u> the subject of this equation: $\quad \text{speed} = \dfrac{\text{distance}}{\text{time}}$

1) <u>Multiply</u> both sides by <u>time</u>: $\qquad\qquad\qquad\qquad \text{speed} \times \text{time} = \dfrac{\text{distance} \times \text{time}}{\text{time}}$

2) Time is now on the top <u>and</u> the bottom of the fraction, so it cancels out: $\qquad\qquad\qquad\qquad\qquad\quad \text{speed} \times \text{time} = \dfrac{\text{distance} \times \cancel{\text{time}}}{\cancel{\text{time}}}$

3) This leaves <u>distance</u> by itself. So it's the <u>subject</u>: $\qquad \text{speed} \times \text{time} = \text{distance}$

Tiny or **Huge** Quantities Often use **Standard Form**

1) The quantities to do with atoms are <u>really tiny</u>, so they're written in <u>standard form</u>. E.g. the radius of an atom is about 1×10^{-10} m (see page 73).

2) <u>Big quantities</u> are often written in <u>standard form</u> too — e.g. the speed of EM waves is 3×10^8 m/s.

A is a number between 1 and 10.

$$A \times 10^n$$

n is the number of places the decimal point would move if you wrote the number out in decimal form.

If n is positive you know you're dealing with a large number. If n is negative you're dealing with a small number.

S.I. units help scientists to compare data...

You can only really <u>compare</u> things if they're in the <u>same units</u>. For example, if you measured the speed of one car in m/s, and one in km/h, it would be hard to know which car was going faster.

Converting Units

You can <u>convert units</u> using <u>prefixes</u>. This can save you from having to write a lot of 0's...

Different Units Help you to Write Large and Small Quantities

1) Quantities come in a huge <u>range</u> of sizes.
2) To make the size of numbers <u>easier to handle</u>, larger or smaller units are used.
3) Larger and smaller units are written as the <u>S.I. base unit</u> with a <u>little word</u> in <u>front</u> (a prefix). Here are some <u>examples</u> of <u>prefixes</u> and what they mean:

Kilogram is an exception. It's an S.I. unit with the prefix already on it.

Prefix	mega (M)	kilo (k)	deci (d)	centi (c)	milli (m)	micro (μ)
Multiple of Unit	1 000 000 times bigger	1000 times bigger	10 times smaller	100 times smaller	1000 times smaller	1 000 000 times smaller

E.g. 1 <u>kilo</u>metre is <u>1000</u> metres.   E.g. there are <u>1000</u> <u>milli</u>metres in 1 metre.

You Need to be Able to Convert Between Units

You need to know how to <u>convert</u> (change) one unit into another.

- To go from a <u>bigger unit</u> (like m) to a <u>smaller unit</u> (like cm), you <u>multiply</u> by the conversion factor.
- To go from a <u>smaller unit</u> (like g) to a <u>bigger unit</u> (like kg), you <u>divide</u> by the conversion factor.

Here are some useful conversions:

Energy can have units of J and kJ.

$$kJ \xrightarrow{\times 1000} J$$
$$\div 1000$$

Mass can have units of kg and g.

$$kg \xrightarrow{\times 1000} g$$
$$\div 1000$$

Volume can have units of m^3 and cm^3.

$$m^3 \xrightarrow{\times 1\,000\,000} cm^3$$
$$\div 1\,000\,000$$

EXAMPLE:

A car has travelled 0.015 kilometres. How many metres has it travelled?

1 km = 1000 m. So to convert from km (a bigger unit) to m (a smaller unit) you need to <u>multiply</u> by 1000.   0.015 km × 1000 = 15 m

Always make sure the values you put into an equation or formula have the right units.

To convert from bigger units to smaller units...

...multiply by the conversion factor. And to convert from <u>smaller units</u> to <u>bigger units</u>, <u>divide</u> by the <u>conversion factor</u>. Don't go getting this rule muddled up and the wrong way round...

Drawing Conclusions

Once you've designed your experiment, carried it out, processed and presented your data, it's finally time to sit down and work out exactly what your data tells you. Time for some fun with conclusions...

You Can **Only Conclude** What the Data Shows and **No More**

1) Drawing conclusions might seem pretty straightforward — you just look at your data and say what pattern or relationship you see between the dependent and independent variables.

The table on the right shows the potential difference across a light bulb for three different currents through the bulb:

Current (A)	Potential difference (V)
6	4
9	10
12	13

CONCLUSION: A higher current through the bulb gives a higher potential difference across the bulb.

2) But you've got to be really careful that your conclusion matches the data you've got and doesn't go any further.

You can't conclude that the potential difference across any circuit component will be higher for a larger current — the results might be completely different.

3) You also need to be able to use your results to justify your conclusion (i.e. back up your conclusion with some specific data).

The potential difference across the bulb was 9 V higher with a current of 12 A compared to a current of 6 A.

4) When writing a conclusion you need to refer back to the original hypothesis and say whether the data supports it or not:

The hypothesis for this experiment might have been that a higher current through the bulb would increase the potential difference across the bulb. If so, the data supports the hypothesis.

You should be able to back up your conclusion with your data...

You should always be able to explain how your data supports your conclusion. It's easy to go too far with conclusions and start making bold claims that your data simply can't back up. When you're drawing conclusions, it's also important that you check back to your initial hypothesis, the one you made right back at the start of the investigation, to see whether your data supports it or not.

Correlation and Cause

Don't get carried away when you're <u>drawing conclusions</u> — <u>correlation</u> doesn't always mean <u>cause</u>. There could be a few reasons why two variables appear to be linked, as you're about to find out.

Correlation does not Mean Cause

If two things are correlated (i.e. there's a relationship between them) it <u>doesn't</u> necessarily mean a change in one variable is <u>causing</u> the change in the other — this is <u>really important</u> — <u>don't forget it</u>.

There are Three Possible Reasons for a Correlation

1) <u>CHANCE</u>: It might seem strange, but two things can show a correlation purely due to <u>chance</u>.

> For example, one study might find a correlation between people's hair colour and how good they are at frisbee. But other scientists <u>don't</u> get a correlation when they investigate it — the results of the first study are just a <u>fluke</u>.

2) <u>LINKED BY A 3RD VARIABLE</u>: A lot of the time it may <u>look</u> as if a change in one variable is causing a change in the other, but it <u>isn't</u> — a <u>third variable links</u> the two things.

> For example, there's a correlation between <u>water temperature</u> and <u>shark attacks</u>. This isn't because warmer water makes sharks crazy. Instead, they're linked by a third variable — the <u>number of people swimming</u> (more people swim when the water's hotter, and with more people in the water you get more shark attacks).

3) <u>CAUSE</u>: Sometimes a change in one variable does <u>cause</u> a change in the other. You can only conclude that a correlation is due to cause when you've <u>controlled all the variables</u> that could, just could, be affecting the result.

> For example, there's a correlation between <u>smoking</u> and <u>lung cancer</u>. This is because chemicals in tobacco smoke cause lung cancer. This conclusion was only made once <u>other variables</u> (such as age and exposure to other things that cause cancer) had been <u>controlled</u>.

Two variables could appear to be linked by chance...

<u>Correlation</u> doesn't necessarily mean <u>cause</u> — two variables might appear to be linked but it could just be down to <u>chance</u>, or they could be linked by a <u>third variable</u>. When you draw conclusions, make sure you're not jumping to conclusions about cause, and check that you properly <u>consider</u> all the reasons why two variables might appear to be linked.

Uncertainty

Uncertainty is how sure you can really be about your data. There's a little bit of maths to do, and also a formula to learn. But don't worry too much — it's no more than a simple bit of subtraction and division.

Uncertainty is the Amount of Error Your Measurements Might Have

1) Measurements you make will have some uncertainty in them (i.e. they won't be completely perfect).

2) This can be due to random errors (see page 8). It can also be due to limits in what your measuring equipment can measure.

3) This means that the mean of your results will have some uncertainty to it.

4) You can calculate the uncertainty of a mean result using this equation:

$$\text{uncertainty} = \frac{\text{range}}{2}$$  The range is the largest value minus the smallest value (p.9).

5) The less precise your results are, the higher the uncertainty will be.

6) Uncertainties are shown using the '±' symbol.

EXAMPLE: The table below shows the results of an experiment to determine the speed of the trolley as it moves along a horizontal surface. Calculate the uncertainty of the mean.

Repeat	1	2	3	4
Speed (m/s)	2.01	1.98	2.00	2.01

1) First work out the range:

Range = 2.01 − 1.98 = 0.030 m/s

2) Then find the mean:

Mean = (2.01 + 1.98 + 2.00 + 2.01) ÷ 4
= 8.00 ÷ 4 = 2.00

3) Use the range to find the uncertainty:

Uncertainty = range ÷ 2 = 0.030 ÷ 2 = 0.015 m/s

So the uncertainty of the mean = 2.00 ± 0.015 m/s

The smaller the uncertainty, the more precise your results...

Remember that equation for uncertainty. You never know when you might need it — you could be expected to use it in the exams. You need to make sure all the data is in the same units though. For example, if you had some measurements in metres, and some in centimetres, you'd need to convert them all into either metres or centimetres before you set about calculating uncertainty.

Evaluation

Hurrah! The end of another investigation. Well, now you have to work out all the things you did <u>wrong</u>. That's what <u>evaluations</u> are all about I'm afraid. Best get cracking with this page...

Evaluations — Describe **How** it Could be **Improved**

In an evaluation you look back over the whole investigation.

1) You should comment on the <u>method</u> — was it <u>valid</u>?
   Did you control all the other variables to make it a <u>fair test</u>?

2) Comment on the <u>quality</u> of the <u>results</u> — was there <u>enough evidence</u> to reach a valid <u>conclusion</u>?
   Were the results <u>repeatable</u>, <u>reproducible</u>, <u>accurate</u> and <u>precise</u>?

3) Were there any <u>anomalous</u> results? If there were <u>none</u> then <u>say so</u>. If there were any,
   try to <u>explain</u> them — were they caused by <u>errors</u> in measurement?

4) You should comment on the level of <u>uncertainty</u> in your results too.

5) Thinking about these things lets you say how <u>confident</u> you are that your conclusion is <u>right</u>.

6) Then you can suggest any <u>changes</u> to the <u>method</u> that would <u>improve</u> the
   quality of the results, so you could have <u>more confidence</u> in your conclusion.

7) For example, taking measurements at <u>narrower intervals</u> could give you a <u>more accurate result</u>. E.g.

> <u>Springs</u> have a <u>limit of proportionality</u> (a maximum force before force and extension
> are no longer proportional). Say you use several <u>identical</u> springs to do an experiment
> to find the limit of proportionality of the springs. If you apply forces of 1 N, 2 N, 3 N,
> 4 N and 5 N, and from the results see that it is somewhere <u>between 4 N and 5 N</u>, you
> could <u>repeat</u> the experiment with one of the other springs, taking <u>more measurements</u>
> <u>between 4 N and 5 N</u> to get a <u>more accurate</u> value for the limit of proportionality.

8) You could also make more <u>predictions</u> based on your conclusion.
   You could then carry out <u>further experiments</u> to test the new predictions.

Always look for ways to improve your investigations...

So there you have it — <u>Working Scientifically</u>. Make sure you know this stuff like the back of your hand. It's not just in the lab, when you're carrying out your groundbreaking <u>investigations</u>, that you'll need to know how to work scientifically. You can be asked about it in the <u>exams</u> as well. So swot up...

Energy Stores

Energy is never used up. It's just the way that it's stored that changes.
There are eight energy stores you need to know about, so let's get cracking...

Energy is Transferred Between Energy Stores

Energy is stored in the different energy stores of an object.
You need to know the following energy stores:

1) KINETIC — anything moving has energy in its kinetic energy store.

2) THERMAL — all objects have energy in this store.
   The hotter the object, the more energy in the store.

You may also see thermal energy stores called internal energy stores.

3) CHEMICAL — anything that can release energy by a chemical reaction has energy in this store, e.g. food.

4) GRAVITATIONAL POTENTIAL — any object raised above ground level has energy in this store.

5) ELASTIC POTENTIAL — anything stretched has energy in this store, like springs and rubber bands.

6) ELECTROSTATIC — e.g. two charges that attract or repel each other have energy in this store.

7) MAGNETIC — e.g. two magnets that attract or repel each other have energy in this store.

8) NUCLEAR — the nucleus of an atom releases energy from this store in nuclear reactions.

You'll learn more about nuclear reactions on pages 76-77.

EXAM TIP

No matter what store it's in, it's all energy...

In the exam, make sure you refer to energy in terms of the store it's in. For example, if you're describing energy in a hot object, say it 'has energy in its thermal energy store'.

Energy Transfer

Now you know about the different energy stores, it's time to find out how energy is <u>transferred</u> between them.

Energy can be Transferred in Four Ways

MECHANICALLY
1) This happens when a <u>force does work</u> (p.87) on an object.
2) For example, a force <u>pushing</u> an object along the floor.

ELECTRICALLY
1) This happens when a <u>moving charge does work</u> (p.57).
2) For example, when a <u>current flows</u> through a <u>light bulb</u>.

BY HEATING
1) When energy is transferred from a <u>hotter</u> object to a <u>colder</u> object.
2) For example, when a pan of water is <u>heated</u> on a hob.

BY RADIATION
1) This happens when energy is transferred by e.g. <u>sound</u> or <u>light</u>.
2) For example, when energy from the <u>Sun</u> travels to <u>Earth</u> by <u>light</u>.

When a System Changes, Energy is Transferred

1) A <u>system</u> is just the <u>single</u> object or a <u>group</u> of <u>objects</u> that you're interested in.
2) When a system <u>changes</u>, the way energy is <u>stored</u> changes in one of the ways above.
3) <u>Closed systems</u> are systems where <u>no matter</u> (stuff) or <u>energy</u> can <u>enter or leave</u>.
4) When a closed system changes, there is no <u>net (overall) change</u> in the <u>total energy</u> of the system.
5) For example...

> A <u>cold spoon</u> sealed in a flask of <u>hot soup</u> is a closed system.
>
> Energy is <u>transferred</u> from the thermal energy store of the <u>soup</u> to the thermal energy store of the <u>spoon</u> by heating.
>
> But <u>no energy</u> leaves the system. The total energy <u>stays the same</u>.

Heating a Material Transfers Energy to its Thermal Energy Store

1) As a material is <u>heated</u>, energy is <u>transferred</u> to its <u>thermal</u> energy store.
2) This causes its <u>temperature to increase</u>.
3) You need to be able to <u>describe</u> the changes in how energy is stored when an object is <u>heated</u>.
4) For example, if you <u>boil water in an electric kettle</u>:

> Energy is transferred <u>electrically</u> to the <u>thermal</u> energy store of the kettle's heating element.
>
> Energy is then transferred <u>by heating</u> to the water's <u>thermal</u> energy store.
>
> So the <u>temperature</u> of the water <u>increases</u>.

Don't talk about 'electrical energy stores'...

It's easy to accidentally refer to <u>electrical energy stores</u>, rather than talk about how <u>energy</u> is <u>transferred electrically</u>. Make sure you don't get it mixed up the exam.

Mechanical Energy Transfer

It's time to look at <u>mechanical energy transfers</u> a bit more. They happen when a <u>force does work</u>.

Forces Cause Mechanical Energy Transfers

1) If a <u>force</u> moves an object, then <u>work is done</u>.

There's more on work done on p.87.

2) Work done is <u>the same</u> as energy transferred.

3) So energy is transferred <u>mechanically</u> when a force moves an object.

4) For any given situation, you'll have to <u>describe</u> the changes in how energy is <u>stored</u>.

5) Here are a few <u>examples</u>:

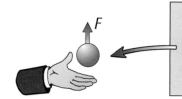

Example 1 — A ball <u>thrown into the air</u>
A boy throws a ball <u>upwards</u>. The boy <u>exerts a force</u> on the ball.
Energy is transferred <u>mechanically</u> from the <u>chemical</u> energy store of the boy's <u>arm</u> to the <u>kinetic</u> energy stores of the <u>ball and arm</u>.

Example 2 — A ball <u>dropped from a height</u>
The ball is <u>accelerated</u> by the <u>constant force</u> of <u>gravity</u>.
Energy is <u>transferred mechanically</u> from the ball's <u>gravitational potential energy</u> store to its <u>kinetic</u> energy store.

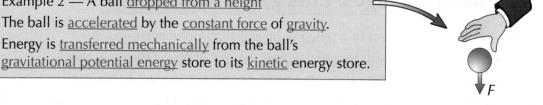

Example 3 — A car <u>slowing down</u>
<u>Friction</u> acts between the car's <u>brakes</u> and its <u>wheels</u>.
Energy is transferred <u>mechanically</u> from the <u>wheels' kinetic energy</u> stores to the <u>thermal</u> energy store of the <u>surroundings</u>.

frictional forces cause a transfer of energy

Example 4 — A car <u>hitting a wall</u>
When the <u>car</u> and the <u>wall touch</u>, there is a <u>normal contact force</u> (p.85) on both of them.
Energy is transferred <u>mechanically</u> from the car's <u>kinetic</u> energy store to <u>lots</u> of other energy stores.
Some energy is transferred to the <u>elastic potential</u> and <u>thermal</u> energy stores of the <u>wall</u> and the <u>car</u>.
Some energy might also be <u>transferred away</u> by <u>sound</u> waves.

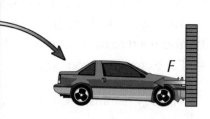

REVISION TIP

Energy is transferred between the different stores of objects...

Energy stores pop up <u>everywhere</u> in physics. You need to be able to describe <u>how energy is transferred</u>, and <u>which stores</u> it gets transferred between, for <u>any scenario</u>. So, make sure you know all the <u>energy stores</u> and <u>transfer methods</u> like the back of your hand.

Kinetic and Potential Energy Stores

Kinetic, gravitational potential and elastic potential are three important energy stores.
Here's how to calculate the amount of energy in each of them.

Movement Means Energy in an Object's Kinetic Energy Store

1) Energy is transferred <u>to</u> the kinetic energy store when an object <u>speeds up</u>.

2) Energy is transferred <u>away</u> from this store when an object <u>slows down</u>.

3) There's a <u>slightly tricky</u> formula for finding the energy in an object's kinetic energy store:

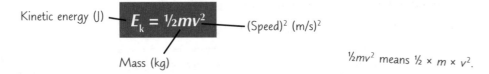

Kinetic energy (J) — $E_k = \frac{1}{2}mv^2$ — (Speed)^2 (m/s)^2

Mass (kg)

$\frac{1}{2}mv^2$ means $\frac{1}{2} \times m \times v^2$.

EXAMPLE:

A car of mass 2500 kg is travelling at 20 m/s. Calculate the energy in its kinetic energy store.

$E_k = \frac{1}{2} \times 2500 \times 20^2 = 500\,000$ J

Raised Objects Store Energy in Gravitational Potential Energy Stores

1) All objects raised <u>above the ground</u> gain energy in their <u>gravitational potential energy</u> (g.p.e.) store.

2) You can find the <u>energy</u> in an object's g.p.e. store using:

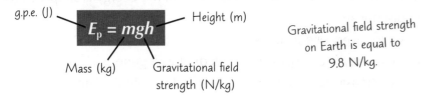

g.p.e. (J) — $E_p = mgh$ — Height (m)

Mass (kg)   Gravitational field strength (N/kg)

Gravitational field strength on Earth is equal to 9.8 N/kg.

Stretching can Transfer Energy to Elastic Potential Energy Stores

1) <u>Stretching</u> or <u>squashing</u> an object can transfer energy to its <u>elastic potential energy store</u>.

2) The energy in the <u>elastic potential energy store</u> of a stretched spring can be found using:

Elastic potential energy (J) — $E_e = \frac{1}{2}ke^2$ — (Extension)^2 (m)^2

Spring constant (N/m)

3) This equation only works if the <u>limit of proportionality</u> has not been <u>passed</u> (p.90).

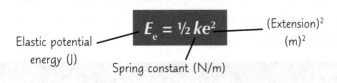

Greater height means more energy in gravitational potential stores...

Wow, that's a lot of equations on a single page... As with all equations you come across, make sure you know what all the <u>variables</u> in them are, as well as what <u>units</u> all the variables in the equations are in.

Conservation of Energy

Repeat after me: energy is NEVER destroyed. Make sure you learn that fact, it's really important.

Energy is Always Wasted in any Energy Transfer

1) When energy is transferred between stores, some energy is transferred to the store you want it in.
2) This energy is usefully transferred.
3) But in any energy transfer, some energy is always dissipated.
4) This means the energy is transferred to useless stores.
5) These useless energy stores are usually thermal energy stores.
6) This energy is often described as 'wasted' energy.

When you use a mobile phone, energy is transferred from the chemical energy store of the battery.
Some energy is usefully transferred.
But some is dissipated to the thermal energy store of the phone.

You Need to Know the Conservation of Energy Principle

Energy can be transferred usefully, stored or dissipated, but can never be created or destroyed.

1) This means that whenever a system changes, all the energy is simply moved between stores.
2) It never disappears.
3) This is true for every energy transfer.
4) Even when energy is dissipated (or wasted), it isn't gone.
5) It's just been transferred to an energy store that we didn't want.
6) Ways of reducing unwanted energy transfers are given on p.29.

You Can Calculate Energy Transfers Using Conservation of Energy

You can make calculations when energy is transferred between two stores. For example:

1) You saw on p.20 that a falling object transfers energy from its g.p.e. store to its kinetic energy store.
2) The conservation of energy principle (above) says that energy can't be destroyed.
3) So for a falling object when there's no air resistance:

Energy lost from the g.p.e. store = Energy gained in the kinetic energy store

Energy is always conserved, but it can be wasted...

The energy transferred away from a falling object's gravitational potential energy store is only equal to the energy gained in its kinetic energy store if there's no air resistance. In reality, some energy would be wasted. For example, some energy would be transferred mechanically to the thermal energy stores of the air.

Specific Heat Capacity

Specific heat capacity is really just a sciencey way of saying how hard it is to heat something up...

Different Materials Have Different Specific Heat Capacities

1) Some materials need more energy to increase their temperature than others.
2) These materials also transfer more energy when they cool down again.
3) They can 'store' a lot of energy.
4) The amount of energy stored or released as a material changes temperature depends on the specific heat capacity of the material:

> Specific heat capacity is the amount of energy needed to raise the temperature of 1 kg of a material by 1 °C.

There's a Helpful Formula Involving Specific Heat Capacity

Below is the equation that links energy transferred to specific heat capacity (the Δ's just mean "change in").

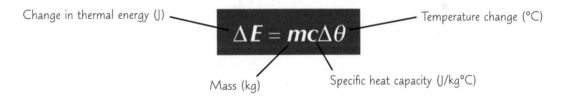

Change in thermal energy (J) — $\Delta E = mc\Delta\theta$ — Temperature change (°C)

Mass (kg)   Specific heat capacity (J/kg°C)

EXAMPLE:

A hot block of metal cools from 55 °C to 25 °C. The block has a mass of 0.50 kg and is made from a material that has a specific heat capacity of 320 J/kg°C. Calculate the energy transferred from the block as it cooled.

1) First, calculate the change in the block's temperature.　　55 °C − 25 °C = 30 °C

2) The numbers are in the correct units.　　　　　　　　　$\Delta E = mc\Delta\theta$
   So put them into the equation.　　　　　　　　　　　　= 0.50 × 320 × 30

3) The unit for energy is joules (J).　　　　　　　　　　　= 4800 J

If you're not working out the energy, you'll have to rearrange the equation, so a formula triangle will come in dead handy. To use them, cover up the thing you want to find and write down what's left showing.

You write the bits of the formula in the triangle like this:

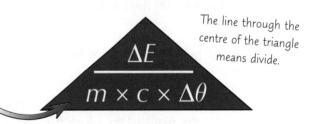

The line through the centre of the triangle means divide.

$$\frac{\Delta E}{m \times c \times \Delta\theta}$$

Some substances can store more energy than others...

Water is a substance that can store a lot of energy in its thermal stores — it has a high specific heat capacity. This is lucky for us as our bodies are mostly water. It'd be unfortunate if we started boiling on a hot day. Learn the definition of specific heat capacity and make sure you know how to use the formula involving it.

PRACTICAL Investigating Specific Heat Capacity

Time for a _practical_. Woohoo I hear you shout! Maybe not, but you do have to know it I'm afraid.

Investigate the Specific Heat Capacity of a **Solid Block**

1) Measure the _mass_ of the _block_.

2) Wrap it in an insulating layer (e.g. thick newspaper) to reduce _energy losses_.

3) Set up the _apparatus_ as shown.

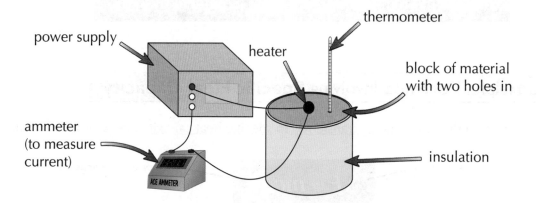

4) Measure the _starting temperature_ of the block.

5) _Turn on_ the power supply and _start_ a _stopwatch_.

6) Record the _potential difference_, _V_, of the power supply and the _current_, _I_. They shouldn't change at all.

7) After _10 minutes_, take a reading of the block's _temperature_.

8) Turn off the heater and work out the _temperature change_.

9) Calculate the power of the heater using _P = VI_ (p.58).

10) You can use this to calculate the _specific heat capacity_ of the _material_ the block is made from (see the next page).

Think about how you could improve your experiments...

If the hole in your material is _bigger_ than your _thermometer_, you could put a small amount of water in the hole with the thermometer. This helps the thermometer to measure the temperature of the block more accurately, as water is a better thermal conductor than _air_.

Investigating Specific Heat Capacity  PRACTICAL

You're not quite done yet — now that the fiddly bit is over, it's time to whip your calculator out to find the <u>specific heat capacity</u> of the <u>material</u> from your results.

Calculating the **Specific Heat Capacity**

To calculate the <u>specific heat capacity</u> from your results from the previous page, you need ideas about <u>work done</u> and <u>energy transferred</u>:

1) When you turn on the power, the <u>current</u> in the circuit <u>does work</u> on the heater.
2) Energy is transferred <u>electrically</u> from the power supply to the heater's <u>thermal energy store</u>.
3) The energy transferred to the heater is given by $E = Pt$ (p.28).
   (P is the <u>power</u> of the <u>heater</u> and t is <u>how long</u> the heater is on for.)
4) This energy is then transferred to the material's <u>thermal</u> energy store <u>by heating</u>.
5) So the value of E you calculated in step 3 is equal to the change in thermal energy of the block, ΔE, and you can use it to find the <u>specific heat capacity</u> of the block, c.
6) <u>Rearrange the equation</u> from page 23 to give you $c = \Delta E \div (m \times \Delta\theta)$, and put in your results.
7) The <u>temperature change</u>, $\Delta\theta$, and <u>mass</u>, m, were <u>measured</u> in the experiment.
   Use your value of E from step 3 as ΔE.

This example shows how to do the calculation:

EXAMPLE:

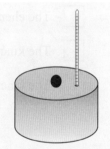

A 1.0 kg block of material is heated using a 10 V power supply.
The starting temperature of the block is 20 °C.
The current through the heater is recorded as 10 A.
After 60 seconds, the final temperature of the block is 26 °C.
Calculate the specific heat capacity of the material of the block.

1) Calculate the <u>power</u> of the heater. $P = V \times I = 10 \times 10 = 100$ W
2) Calculate the <u>energy transferred</u>. $E = P \times t = 100 \times 60 = 6000$ J
3) Find the <u>change in temperature</u>. $\Delta\theta = 26 - 20 = 6$ °C
4) Calculate the <u>specific heat capacity</u>. $c = \Delta E \div (m \times \Delta\theta) = 6000 \div (1.0 \times 6) = 1000$ J/kg °C

You Can Find the **Specific Heat Capacities** of **Liquids** Too

1) You can <u>repeat</u> the experiment shown on the previous page with <u>different materials</u> to see how their specific heat capacities <u>compare</u>.
2) For a <u>liquid</u>, place the <u>heater</u> and <u>thermometer</u> into an <u>insulated beaker</u> with a <u>known mass</u> of the liquid.
3) Then carry out the rest of the experiment in <u>exactly the same way</u> as above.

Insulation reduces the energy transferred to the surroundings...

If you repeat the experiment with a <u>liquid</u>, don't let it start <u>boiling</u> as this will affect your results. Look up the <u>boiling point</u> of the liquid, and then monitor its temperature throughout the experiment to check that it doesn't get too close to the boiling point.

Warm-Up & Exam Questions

These questions give you chance to use your knowledge about energy transfers and specific heat capacity.

Warm-Up Questions

1) Give two ways in which energy can be transferred.
2) Describe how energy is transferred between stores as someone throws a ball upwards.
3) True or false? The energy in an object's gravitational potential energy store is proportional to its mass.
4) Which has more energy in its kinetic energy store: a person walking at 3 miles per hour, or a lorry travelling at 60 miles per hour?
5) State the principle of the conservation of energy.

Exam Questions

1   An electric heater is placed in a hole in a metal block and switched on.   (Grade 1-3)
     Energy is transferred from the thermal energy store of the heater.
     Where is the energy transferred to? Tick **one** box.

     ☐   The thermal energy store of the metal block

     ☐   The chemical energy store of the heater

     ☐   The kinetic energy store of the metal block

     ☐   The kinetic energy store of the heater

     [1 mark]

2   This question is about energy transfers. (Grade 3-4)

     Draw one line from each scenario to the energy store that energy is transferred away from.

     | A skydiver falling from an aeroplane. | | elastic potential |
     | A substance undergoing a nuclear reaction. | | gravitational potential |
     | A piece of burning coal. | | chemical |
     | | nuclear |

     [3 marks]

Exam Questions

3   **Figure 1** shows a toy car that is launched by pulling it backwards onto a spring.
The spring compresses, and then the car is released.

Figure 1

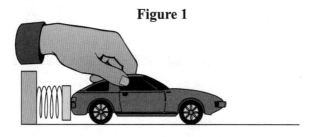

3.1   Name the store that energy is transferred from as the car is released.

[1 mark]

Immediately after the launch, the car moves away at a speed of 0.9 m/s.
The car has a mass of 0.20 kg.

3.2   Write down the equation that links the energy in an object's kinetic energy store, mass and speed.

[1 mark]

3.3   Calculate the energy in the kinetic energy store of the car immediately after it is released.

[2 marks]

4   A motor lifts a load of mass 20 kg.
The load gains 137.2 J of energy in its gravitational potential energy store.

4.1   Write down the equation that links the energy in an object's gravitational potential energy store,
mass, gravitational field strength and height.

[1 mark]

4.2   Calculate the height through which the motor lifts the load.
Assume the gravitational field strength = 9.8 N/kg

[3 marks]

4.3   The motor releases the load and the load falls.
Ignoring air resistance, describe the changes in the way energy is stored that take place
as the load falls.

[2 marks]

4.4   Describe how your answer to **4.3** would differ if air resistance was not ignored.

[1 mark]

5   36 000 J of energy is transferred to change the temperature of a 0.5 kg concrete block by 80 °C.

Calculate the specific heat capacity of the concrete block in J/kg °C.
Use the correct equation from the Physics Equation Sheet on the inside back cover.

[3 marks]

Power

The more powerful a device is, the more energy it will transfer in a certain amount of time.

Power is the 'Rate of Doing Work'

1) Power is the rate of energy transfer.
2) You can also say it's the rate of doing work.
3) This just means that power is how fast energy is transferred or how fast work is done.
4) Power is measured in watts.
5) One watt = 1 joule of energy transferred per second.
6) You can calculate power using these equations:

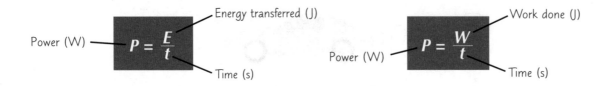

Energy transferred (J)

Power (W) — $P = \dfrac{E}{t}$

Time (s)

Work done (J)

Power (W) — $P = \dfrac{W}{t}$

Time (s)

> Take two cars that are the same in every way apart from the power of their engines. Both cars race the same distance along a straight race track to a finish line. The car with the more powerful engine will reach the finish line faster than the other car. This is because it will transfer the same amount of energy but over a shorter time.

EXAMPLE:

**a) It takes 8000 J of work to lift a stuntman to the top of a building.
A motor takes 50 s to make the lift.
Calculate the power of the motor.**

1) The numbers are in the correct units.
2) Put the numbers into the equation for power in terms of work.

$P = W \div t$
$= 8000 \div 50$
$= 160 \text{ W}$

**b) A second motor has a power of 200 W.
It lifts the stuntman for 30 s.
Calculate the energy transferred by the motor.**

1) Rearrange the power equation for energy transferred.
2) Put the numbers in.
3) Remember energy is in joules.

$P = E \div t \text{ so } E = P \times t$
$= 200 \times 30$
$= 6000 \text{ J}$

A large power doesn't always mean a large force...

A powerful device is not necessarily one which can exert a strong force (although it usually ends up that way). A powerful device is one which transfers a lot of energy in a short space of time.

Reducing Unwanted Energy Transfers

There are a few ways you can <u>reduce</u> the amount of energy running off to a <u>completely useless</u> store.

Lubrication Reduces Frictional Forces

1) <u>Friction</u> acts between all objects that <u>rub together</u>.
2) This causes some energy in the system to be <u>dissipated</u>.
3) <u>Lubricants</u> can be used to <u>reduce the friction</u> between the objects.
4) For example, <u>oil</u> in <u>car engines</u> reduces friction between all of the moving parts.
5) This <u>reduces</u> the amount of <u>dissipated energy</u>.

Insulation Has a Low Thermal Conductivity

1) When part of a material is <u>heated</u>, that part of the material gains <u>energy</u>.
2) This energy is <u>transferred</u> across the material so that the rest of the material gets <u>warmer</u>.
3) For example, if you heated <u>one end</u> of a <u>metal rod</u>, the <u>other end</u> would <u>eventually</u> get warmer. This is known as <u>conduction</u>.
4) <u>Thermal conductivity</u> is a measure of how <u>quickly</u> energy is transferred by conduction through a material.
5) Materials with a <u>high thermal conductivity</u> transfer <u>lots</u> of energy in a <u>short time</u>.
6) Materials with a <u>low thermal conductivity</u> are called <u>thermal insulators</u>.
7) Thermal insulators can reduce unwanted transfers <u>by heating</u>, e.g. in the <u>home</u>.

Insulation is Important for Keeping Buildings Warm

You can keep your home cosy and <u>warm</u> by <u>reducing</u> the <u>rate of cooling</u>.
How <u>quickly</u> a building cools depends on:

1) How <u>thick</u> its <u>walls</u> are. The <u>thicker</u> the walls are, the <u>slower</u> a building will <u>cool</u>.
2) The <u>thermal conductivity</u> of its walls. Building walls from a material with a <u>low thermal conductivity</u> reduces the rate of cooling.
3) How much <u>thermal insulation</u> there is, e.g. <u>loft insulation</u> reduces energy losses through the roof.

Energy Transfers Involve Some Wasted Energy

1) You saw on page 22 that some energy is always wasted when energy is transferred.
2) The <u>less energy</u> that is <u>wasted</u>, the <u>more efficient</u> the energy transfer is.
3) The <u>efficiency</u> of an energy transfer is a measure of the amount of energy that ends up in <u>useful</u> energy stores.
4) But as <u>some</u> energy is <u>always</u> wasted, <u>nothing is 100% efficient</u>.

How to calculate the efficiency of a transfer is on the next page.

Having a well-insulated home can reduce your heating bills...

When people talk of <u>energy loss</u>, it's <u>not</u> that the energy has disappeared. It still exists (see page 22), just not in the <u>store</u> we'd like it to be. For example, in a car, you want the energy to transfer to the <u>kinetic energy store</u> of the wheels, and not to the <u>thermal energy stores</u> of the moving components.

Efficiency

Devices have <u>energy transferred</u> to them, but only transfer <u>some</u> of that energy to <u>useful energy stores</u>. Wouldn't it be great if we could tell <u>how much</u> it <u>usefully transfers</u>? That's where <u>efficiency</u> comes in.

There Are **Two Efficiency Equations**

1) The efficiency for any energy transfer can be <u>worked out</u> using this equation:

$$\text{Efficiency} = \frac{\text{Useful output energy transfer}}{\text{Total input energy transfer}}$$

This gives efficiency as a decimal, but you can turn it into a percentage — see below.

EXAMPLE:

36 000 J of energy is transferred to a television. It transfers 28 800 J of this energy usefully. Calculate the efficiency of the television. Give your answer as a percentage.

1) Put the numbers you're given <u>into the equation</u>.

2) To change a <u>decimal</u> to a <u>percentage</u>, <u>multiply</u> your answer <u>by 100</u>.

efficiency = useful output energy transfer
÷ total input energy transfer
= 28 800 ÷ 36 000
= 0.8
0.8 × 100 = 80, so efficiency = 80%

2) You might not know the <u>energy</u> input and output of a device.

3) But you can use its <u>power input</u> and <u>output</u> to calculate its <u>efficiency</u>:

$$\text{Efficiency} = \frac{\text{Useful power output}}{\text{Total power input}}$$

EXAMPLE:

A blender is 70% efficient. It has a total input power of 600 W. Calculate the useful power output.

1) Change the <u>efficiency</u> from a <u>percentage</u> to a <u>decimal</u>. To do this, <u>divide</u> the percentage <u>by 100</u>.

2) <u>Rearrange</u> the equation for <u>useful power output</u>.

3) <u>Stick in</u> the numbers and find the useful power output.

efficiency = 70% ÷ 100 = 0.7

useful power output = efficiency × total power input
useful power output = 0.7 × 600 = 420 W

You might need to calculate the useful output energy transfer...

If you get a tricky exam question, you could be given the amount of energy that is <u>wasted</u> by a device rather than the output energy that is transferred <u>usefully</u>. You can work out the useful output energy by <u>subtracting</u> the wasted energy from the total input energy.

Warm-Up & Exam Questions

Don't let your energy dissipate. These questions will let you see how efficient your revision has been.

Warm-Up Questions

1) What is power?
2) What is 1 watt equivalent to: 1 J, 1 Js or 1 J/s?
3) What should you consider when choosing a material to build house walls from to minimise the rate of cooling?
4) Which has a greater rate of energy transfer: a material with a high thermal conductivity or a material with a low thermal conductivity?
5) Why is the efficiency of an appliance always less than 100%?

Exam Questions

1   The motor of an electric scooter moves the scooter along a flat, horizontal *(Grade 3-4)* course in 20 seconds. During this time the motor does 1 kJ of work.

1.1   Write down the equation that links power, work done and time.

[1 mark]

1.2   Calculate the power of the motor.

[2 marks]

1.3   Suggest **one** way in which unwanted energy transfers in the scooter could be reduced.

[1 mark]

1.4   The scooter's motor is replaced with a more powerful, but otherwise identical, motor. It moves along the same course. How will the performance of the scooter differ from before? Tick **one** box.

☐ It will be faster.   ☐ It will be slower.   ☐ It will use less energy.   ☐ It will use more energy.

[1 mark]

2   An electric fan transfers 7250 J of energy. 2 kJ of this is wasted energy. *(Grade 4-5)*

2.1   Suggest **one** way in which energy is wasted by the fan.

[1 mark]

The useful output energy of the fan is given by the equation below:

useful output energy transfer = total input energy transfer – wasted output energy transfer

2.2   Calculate the energy that is usefully transferred by the fan.

[2 marks]

2.3   The efficiency of a device is given by the equation below:

$$\text{efficiency} = \frac{\text{useful output energy transfer}}{\text{total input energy transfer}}$$

Calculate the efficiency of the fan. Give your answer to **two** significant figures.

[2 marks]

Energy Resources and their Uses

There are lots of energy resources available on Earth. They are either renewable or non-renewable resources.

Non-Renewable Energy Resources Will **Run Out** One Day

1) Non-renewable energy resources are fossil fuels and nuclear fuel.
2) The three main fossil fuels are coal, oil and (natural) gas.
3) We can't replace non-renewable energy resources as quickly as we're using them.

Renewable Energy Resources Will **Never** Run Out

1) Renewable energy resources can be replenished (replaced) as quickly as they are being used.
2) The renewable energy resources you need to know are:

1) The Sun (Solar)	3) Water waves	5) Biofuels	7) Geothermal
2) Wind	4) Hydro-electricity	6) Tides	

Energy Resources can be Used for **Transport**...

1) Transport uses both renewable and non-renewable energy resources. For example:

NON-RENEWABLE ENERGY RESOURCES
Petrol or diesel is used in most vehicles. They're both created from oil.
Coal is used in steam trains to boil water to produce steam.

RENEWABLE ENERGY RESOURCES
Vehicles can run on pure biofuels (p.33) or a mix of a biofuel and petrol or diesel.

2) Electricity can also be used for transport — e.g. electric cars and some trains.
3) The electricity can be generated using renewable or non-renewable energy resources (p.33-37).

...And for **Heating**

Energy resources are also needed for heating things, like your home.

NON-RENEWABLE ENERGY RESOURCES
Natural gas is burnt to heat water in a boiler. This hot water is then pumped into radiators.
Gas fires burn natural gas to heat rooms.
Coal is burnt in open fireplaces.
Electric heaters use electricity which can be generated from non-renewable energy resources.

RENEWABLE ENERGY RESOURCES
Biofuel boilers work in the same way as gas boilers.
A geothermal heat pump uses geothermal energy resources (p.35) to heat buildings.
Solar water heaters use the Sun to heat water which is then pumped into radiators in the building.
Electric heaters can use electricity generated from renewable resources.

Fossil fuels are produced over millions of years — quite a wait...
Make sure you know the difference between renewable and non-renewable energy resources.

Biofuels

Biofuels are a promising renewable energy resource, as they can be <u>used</u> and <u>stored</u> in much the same way as <u>fossil fuels</u>. However, they need a lot of <u>space</u> to grow...

You Need to Be Able to **Compare Resources**

1) You're about to learn all about the <u>main energy resources</u>.

2) You need to be able to:

- describe their effects on the <u>environment</u> (e.g. pollution).
- compare their <u>reliability</u> (whether they can be <u>trusted</u> to provide energy when we need it).

No energy resource is 100% reliable as power plants may unexpectedly break or need to be shut down.

3) So make sure you're <u>paying attention</u>.

Biofuels are Made from **Plants** and **Waste**

1) <u>Biofuels</u> are fuels created from <u>plant</u> products or <u>animal dung</u>.

2) They can be burnt to produce <u>electricity</u> or used to run <u>cars</u> in the same way as <u>fossil fuels</u>.

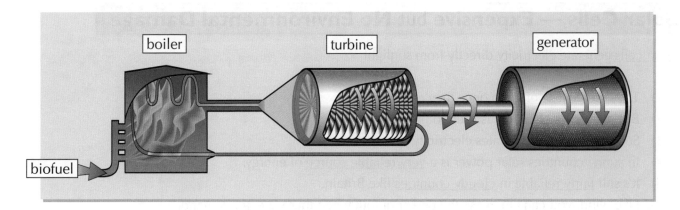

3) They produce <u>carbon dioxide</u> when they're <u>burnt</u>.

4) But the plants used to make biofuels will have <u>absorbed</u> a lot of carbon dioxide while they were <u>growing</u>.

5) In some places, large areas of <u>forest</u> have been <u>cleared</u> to make room to grow <u>biofuels</u>.

6) This leads to lots of animals losing their <u>natural habitats</u>.

7) Crops can be grown <u>throughout the year</u>.

8) Extra biofuels can be constantly produced and <u>stored</u> for when they are needed.

9) So biofuels are fairly <u>reliable</u>.

In theory, biofuels are carbon neutral...

You've probably heard that releasing carbon dioxide (CO_2) into the atmosphere is bad as it leads to <u>global warming</u>. When you <u>burn biofuels</u>, you do <u>release</u> CO_2 into the atmosphere. But, when the plants grew, they <u>absorbed</u> this CO_2 from the atmosphere for <u>photosynthesis</u>. This is why biofuels are often said to be '<u>carbon neutral</u>'.

Wind Power and Solar Power

Coming up are two of the most visible renewable energy resources — <u>wind</u> and <u>solar power</u>.

Wind Power — Lots of Wind Turbines

1) <u>Wind turbines</u> are usually put up in <u>open spaces</u>.
2) When the wind <u>turns the blades</u>, electricity is produced.
3) They produce <u>no pollution</u> once they're built.
4) And they do <u>no permanent</u> (lasting) <u>damage</u> to the landscape. If you <u>remove</u> the turbines, the area goes <u>back to normal</u>.
5) However, they're <u>not as reliable</u> as other energy resources.
6) They don't produce electricity <u>when the wind stops</u>.
7) Turbines are also stopped if the wind is <u>too strong</u>. This stops them getting <u>damaged</u>.
8) It's also <u>impossible</u> to <u>increase supply</u> when there's <u>extra demand</u> (p.59) for electricity.

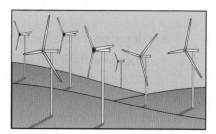

Solar Cells — Expensive but No Environmental Damage

<u>Solar cells</u> generate electricity directly from sunlight.

1) They create <u>no pollution</u> once they're built.
2) But quite a lot of energy is used to <u>build them</u>.
3) Solar power <u>only</u> generates electricity <u>during the day</u>.
4) In <u>sunny</u> countries solar power is a <u>very reliable source</u> of energy.
5) It's still <u>fairly reliable</u> in <u>cloudy countries</u> like Britain.
6) Like wind, you <u>can't increase the power output</u> when there is <u>extra demand</u>.

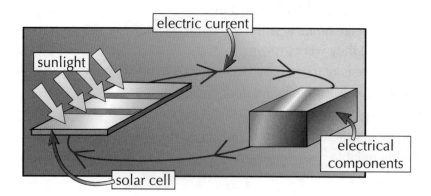

People love the idea of wind power — just not in their back yard...

It's easy to think that renewables are the answer to the world's energy problems. However, they have their <u>downsides</u>, and we definitely <u>couldn't</u> rely on them totally at present. Make sure you know the <u>pros</u> and <u>cons</u> for <u>wind</u> and <u>solar</u> power because there are more renewables coming up on the next page.

Geothermal and Hydro-electric Power

Here are some more examples of <u>renewable energy resources</u> — <u>geothermal</u> and <u>hydro-electric</u>.
These ones are a bit more <u>reliable</u> than wind and solar — read on to find out why.

Geothermal Power uses Underground Thermal Energy Stores

1) <u>Geothermal power</u> uses energy from the <u>thermal</u> energy stores of <u>hot rocks</u> below the Earth's surface.

2) It can be used to <u>generate electricity</u> or to <u>heat buildings</u>.

3) Geothermal power is very <u>reliable</u> because the hot rocks are <u>always</u> hot.

4) Most geothermal power stations only have a <u>small</u> impact on the <u>environment</u>.

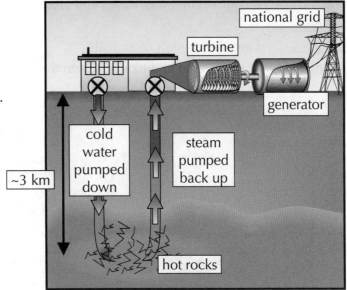

Hydro-electric Power Uses Falling Water

1) <u>Hydro-electric power</u> usually involves building a big <u>dam</u> across a <u>valley</u>.

2) The valley is usually <u>flooded</u>.

3) Water is allowed to flow out <u>through turbines</u>, which generates electricity.

4) There is <u>no pollution</u> when it's running.

5) But there is a <u>big impact</u> on the <u>environment</u> due to the flooding of the valley.

6) Plants rot and release <u>greenhouse gases</u> which lead to global warming (see p.37).

7) Animals and plants also lose <u>their habitats</u> (where they live).

8) There's no problem with <u>reliability</u> in countries that get rain regularly.

9) And it can respond <u>straight away</u> when there's <u>extra demand</u> (p.59) for electricity.

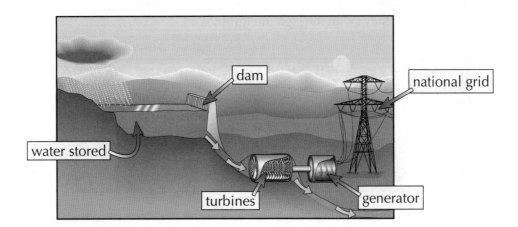

Falling water loses energy from its gravitational potential energy store...

You don't need to be able to <u>describe</u> how these power sources <u>work</u> in detail, but you should be able to comment on their <u>reliability</u> and describe the impact that they have on the <u>environment</u>.

Wave Power and Tidal Barrages

Good ol' water. Not only can we drink it, we can also use it to generate electricity. It's easy to get confused between wave and tidal power as they both involve the seaside — but don't. They are completely different.

Wave Power — Lots of Little Wave-Powered Turbines

1) Turbines around the coast are turned by water waves and electricity is generated.
2) There is no pollution.
3) But they disturb the seabed and the habitats of animals.
4) They are fairly unreliable, as waves tend to die down when the wind drops.

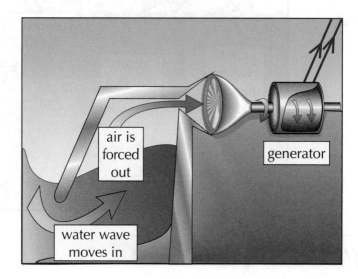

Tidal Barrages Use the Tides of the Sea

1) Tidal barrages are big dams (with turbines in them) built across rivers.
2) Water passing through the turbines generates electricity.
3) The amount of energy generated changes with the tides.
4) But tidal barrages are very reliable, as we can predict the tides (we know what they're going to do).
5) There is no pollution.
6) But they do change the habitat of the wildlife, e.g. birds and sea creatures.
7) And often fish are killed as they swim through the turbines.

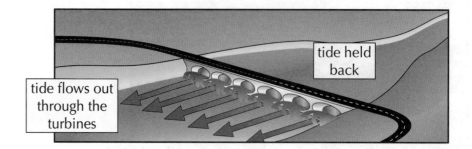

Wave and tidal — power from the motion of the ocean...

The first large-scale tidal barrages started being built in the 1960s, so tidal power isn't a new thing. Wave power is still pretty experimental though. Make sure you can tell the two of them apart.

Non-Renewables

Renewable resources may sound like great news for the environment. But when it comes down to it, they don't currently meet all our needs — so we still need those nasty, polluting non-renewables.

Non-Renewables are Reliable...

1) Fossil fuels and nuclear energy are reliable.

2) There's enough fossil and nuclear fuels to meet current demand.

3) We always have some in stock so power plants can respond quickly to changes in demand.

4) However, these fuels are slowly running out.
   Some fossil fuels may run out within a hundred years.

...But Create Environmental Problems

1) Coal, oil and gas release CO_2 into the atmosphere when they're burned.
   All this CO_2 leads to global warming.

2) Burning coal and oil also releases sulfur dioxide, which causes acid rain.

3) Acid rain makes lakes and rivers acidic, which can kill animals and plants. It can also damage trees and soils.

4) Coal mining makes a mess of the landscape.

5) And it destroys the habitats of local animals and plants.

6) Oil spills cause big environmental problems and harm sea creatures.

7) Nuclear power is clean but the nuclear waste is very dangerous and difficult to get rid of.

8) Nuclear power also carries the risk of a big accident that could release a lot of radiation, like the Fukushima disaster in Japan.

Global warming is where greenhouse gases cause the Earth to warm up.

Radiation can be very dangerous to humans — see p.80-81 for more.

Currently we Still Need Non-Renewables

1) Our use of electricity increased a lot in the 1900s.

2) This was because the population and the number of things that used electricity increased.

3) But electricity use in the UK has been falling slowly since around the year 2000.

4) This is because we're trying harder to be energy efficient and save energy.

5) At the moment, we use non-renewables for most of our electricity, transport and heating.

We're just going to have to deal with non-renewables for now...

Non-renewables cause a lot of long-term problems, but they also have a few short-term advantages. Make sure you can balance up the advantages and disadvantages of fossil and nuclear fuels.

Limitations on the Use of Renewables

Non-renewables may be what we rely on for the vast majority of our energy needs at the moment. But the balance may soon start shifting...

People Want to use **More Renewable** Energy Resources

1) We now know that non-renewables are very bad for the environment and will run out one day (p.37).
2) This makes many people want to use renewable energy resources as they are better for the environment.
3) Many people also think it's better to move to renewables before non-renewables run out.
4) Pressure from other countries and the public has meant that governments have begun to introduce targets for using renewable energy resources.
5) This puts pressure on energy providers to build new renewable power plants. If they don't, they may lose business and money in the future.
6) Car companies have also had to change to become more environmentally-friendly.
7) Cars that can run on electricity are already on the market. The electricity can be generated using renewable energy resources.

The Use of **Renewables** is **Limited** by Lots of **Factors**

1) There's a lot of scientific evidence supporting renewables.
2) But scientists can only give advice. They don't have the power to make people, companies or governments change their ways (see p.4).
3) Moving to renewables can be limited by money.

- Building new renewable power plants costs money.
- Some renewable resources are less reliable than other resources, so a mixture of different resources would need to be used.
- This costs even more money.
- Cars that run on electricity are more expensive than petrol cars.

4) Moving to renewables can also be affected by politics, people and ethics (if something is right or wrong).

- The cost of switching to renewable power will have to be paid through energy bills or taxes.
- Governments often don't want to suggest raising taxes as this may make them unpopular.
- Some people don't want to or can't afford to pay. There are arguments about whether it's ethical (right or wrong) to make them pay.
- Many people also don't want to live near to a power plant (like a wind farm or hydro-electric dam).
- And some think it's not ethical to make people put up with new power plants built near to them.

Going green is on-trend this season...

So with some people wanting to help the environment, others not wanting to be inconvenienced, and greener alternatives being expensive to set up, the energy resources we use are changing. Just not particularly quickly.

Warm-Up & Exam Questions

This is the last set of warm-up and exam questions on Topic 1. They're not *too* horrendous, I promise.

Warm-Up Questions

1) Name two fossil fuels.
2) Explain why solar power is usually less reliable than fossil fuels.
3) Describe one way that renewable energy resources can be used to power vehicles.
4) Give two ways in which using coal as an energy resource causes environmental problems.
5) True or false? Geothermal power is a reliable energy resource.

Exam Questions

1 Which of the following energy resources is a renewable energy resource? Tick **one** box. *(Grade 1-3)*

☐ coal   ☐ nuclear   ☐ wind   ☐ oil

[1 mark]

2 Which of the following is a possible disadvantage of using fossil fuels to generate electricity? Tick **one** box. *(Grade 3-4)*

☐ They cannot generate electricity at night.

☐ They don't release very much energy.

☐ The waste produced is dangerous to dispose of.

☐ They can produce sulfur dioxide and cause acid rain.

[1 mark]

3 Natural gas is a non-renewable energy resource that can be used to generate electricity. *(Grade 4-5)*

3.1 Name **one** other use of natural gas.

[1 mark]

3.2 Give **two** reasons why we still use non-renewable energy resources.

[2 marks]

4 The government of a country needs to generate more electricity to support a growing population. The government has considered using wind, hydro-electric power and tides to generate electricity. *(Grade 4-5)*

4.1* Compare the environmental impact and reliability of wind power and hydro-electric power.

[6 marks]

4.2 The government choose to generate electricity using tidal barrages.
Give **one** environmental advantage of generating electricity using tidal barrages.

[1 mark]

Revision Summary for Topic 1

Well, that's that for <u>Topic 1</u> — this is when you find out <u>how much of it went in</u>.
- Try these questions and <u>tick off each one</u> when you <u>get it right</u>.
- When you've done <u>all the questions</u> under a heading and are <u>completely happy</u> with it, tick it off.

Energy and Specific Heat Capacity (p.18-25) ☑

1) Write down four energy stores. ☑
2) What is a system? ☑
3) What kind of energy store is energy transferred to when you heat an object? ☑
4) Describe the energy transfers that occur as a ball is dropped. ☑
5) If energy is transferred to an object's kinetic energy store, what happens to its speed? ☑
6) Give the equation for finding the energy in an object's gravitational potential energy store. ☑
7) What units must extension, e, be in before it can be used in the equation $E_e = \frac{1}{2}ke^2$? ☑
8) True or false? Energy can be destroyed. ☑
9) What is the definition of the specific heat capacity of a material? ☑
10) Describe an experiment to find the specific heat capacity of a material. ☑

Power and Efficiency (p.28-30) ☑

11) Give two equations you could use to calculate power. ☑
12) How much energy is transferred each second to a 50 W device? ☑
13) How can you reduce unwanted energy transfers in a machine with moving parts? ☑
14) True or false? A good thermal insulator will have a high thermal conductivity. ☑
15) What is meant by the efficiency of an energy transfer? ☑
16) Give the equation that relates efficiency to the useful and total power output. ☑

Energy Resources and Trends in their Use (p.32-38) ☑

17) Name four renewable energy resources and four non-renewable energy resources. ☑
18) Give an example of how a renewable energy resource can be used in homes. ☑
19) Give one environmental issue associated with using biofuels to generate electricity. ☑
20) Give one environmental impact of using wave power to generate electricity. ☑
21) Give one environmental advantage of using nuclear power when compared to power generated from fossil fuels. ☑
22) Explain why the UK is trying to use more renewable energy resources in the future. ☑

Current and Circuit Symbols

Circuit diagrams are a useful way of showing how the <u>components</u> of a circuit are <u>arranged</u>. You need to be able to <u>recognise</u> the <u>symbols</u> used to represent different components. Read on for the complete run down...

Learn these Circuit Diagram Symbols

1) You need to be able to <u>understand circuit diagrams</u> and <u>draw them</u> using the <u>correct symbols</u>.

The parts in a circuit e.g. bulbs, resistors, etc. are called 'components'.

2) These are the <u>symbols</u> you need to know:

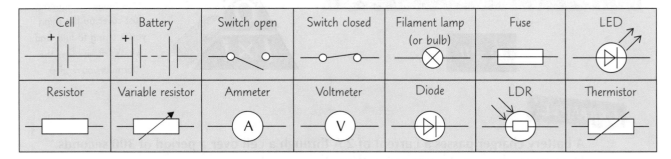

3) Follow these <u>rules</u> to draw a circuit diagram:

- Make sure all the <u>wires</u> in your circuit are <u>straight lines</u>.
- Make sure that the circuit is <u>closed</u>. This means you can follow a wire from one end of the <u>cell</u> or <u>battery</u>, through any <u>components</u>, to the other end of the cell or battery.

Potential Difference Causes Charge to Flow Round a Circuit

1) <u>Electric current</u> is a flow of <u>electrical charge</u>.

- Current is measured in <u>amperes</u>, A.
- Charge is measured in <u>coulombs</u>, C.
- In a <u>single</u>, closed <u>loop</u> the current is the same <u>everywhere</u> in the circuit (see p.51).
- The <u>size</u> of the <u>current</u> tells you <u>how fast</u> the charge is <u>flowing</u>. This is known as the <u>rate of flow of charge</u>.

2) The <u>potential difference</u> is the '<u>driving force</u>' that pushes charge around the circuit.

- Electrical charge will <u>only flow</u> round a complete (closed) circuit if something is providing a <u>potential difference</u>, e.g. a battery.
- Potential difference is measured in <u>volts</u> (<u>V</u>).

'Potential difference' is sometimes called 'voltage'. Exam questions will use 'potential difference', but you can use either.

3) <u>Resistance</u> is anything that <u>slows down</u> the flow of charge.

- Resistance is measured in <u>ohms</u> (Ω).

Charge won't flow without a push...

Left to its own devices, charge won't move anywhere. To get a current flowing, charge needs a 'push'. This push comes in the form of a potential difference, supplied by a source like a cell.

Charge and Resistance Calculations

Prepare yourself to meet two of the most <u>important equations</u> in electricity. They're all about <u>charge</u>, <u>current</u> and <u>potential difference</u>... Now if that doesn't tempt you to read this page, I don't know what will.

Total Charge Through a Circuit Depends on Current and Time

<u>Charge flow</u>, <u>current</u> and <u>time</u> are related by this handy <u>equation</u>:

Charge flow (C) = Current (A) × Time (s)

$$Q = It$$

Use this formula triangle to rearrange the equation. Just cover up the thing you're trying to find, and what's left visible is the formula you're after.

 EXAMPLE:

A battery charger passes a current of 2 A through a cell over a period of 300 seconds. How much charge is transferred to the cell?

Just <u>substitute</u> the values into the equation above and <u>calculate</u> the <u>charge</u>.

$Q = It = 2 \times 300$
$= 600 \text{ C}$

Remember charge is measured in coulombs.

There's a Formula Linking Potential Difference and Current

1) The current flowing <u>through a component</u> depends on the <u>potential difference</u> across it and the <u>resistance</u> of the component.

Resistance measures how much the current is slowed down.

The <u>greater the resistance</u> across a component, the <u>smaller the current</u> that flows (for a <u>given potential difference</u> across the component).

2) The formula linking <u>potential difference (pd)</u> and <u>current</u> is:

Potential Difference (V) = Current (A) × Resistance (Ω)

$$V = IR$$

 EXAMPLE:

A 4.0 Ω resistor in a circuit has a potential difference of 6.0 V across it. What is the current through the resistor?

1) <u>Cover</u> the *I* in the <u>formula triangle</u> to find that <u>$I = V \div R$</u>.

$I = V \div R$

2) <u>Substitute</u> in the values you have, and work out the current.

$I = 6.0 \div 4.0 = 1.5 \text{ A}$

Ohmic Conductors

A circuit component can be either ohmic or non-ohmic. It all depends on whether or not its resistance stays the same when the current is increased. Read on to find out all the details.

Ohmic Conductors Have a Constant Resistance

1) The resistance of an ohmic conductor doesn't change with current.

2) Ohmic conductors only have a fixed resistance if their temperature doesn't change.

3) Wires and resistors are examples of ohmic conductors.

4) $V = IR$ (see p.42), so if resistance is constant, increasing potential difference will lead to an increase in current.

5) So,

> For an ohmic conductor at a fixed temperature, the current flowing through it is directly proportional to the potential difference across it.

6) This means that if you multiply the potential difference by a certain amount, the current will be multiplied by the same amount. For example, if the potential difference doubles, the current doubles too.

Some Components Have a Changing Resistance

The resistance of some components does change with current.
For example, a filament lamp or a diode.

Filament Lamps

1) Filament lamps contain a wire (the filament), which is designed to heat up and 'glow' as the current increases.

2) So as the current increases, the temperature of the filament increases.

3) Resistance increases with temperature, so the resistance increases with current.

A higher current makes a filament glow brighter. So a higher pd means a brighter lamp.

Diodes

1) For diodes, the resistance depends on the direction of the current.

2) A diode will let current flow in one direction. It has a very high resistance in the opposite direction, which makes it hard for a current to flow that way.

Resistance changes when temperature changes...

Remember that ohmic conductors will only have a constant resistance at a constant temperature. In general, resistance increases with temperature (though there are some exceptions, like thermistors — see p.48). So if the temperature is changing, the resistance of your component will be changing too.

Investigating Resistance

Resistance depends on various things. Here's an experiment you can do to investigate one of them
— how the resistance varies with the length of the conductor.

You Can **Investigate** the Factors Affecting **Resistance**

The resistance of a circuit can depend on a number of factors, like whether components
are in series or parallel, p.51 and p.53, or the length of wire used in the circuit.
You can investigate the effect of wire length using the circuit below.

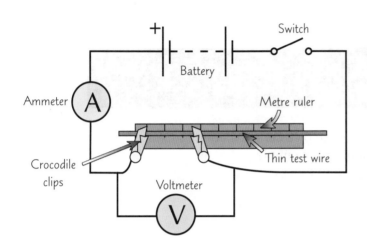

The **Ammeter**

1) Measures the current (in amps) flowing
   through the test wire.

2) The ammeter must always be placed in series
   with whatever you're investigating.

The **Voltmeter**

1) Measures the potential difference
   (or pd) across the test wire (in volts).

2) The voltmeter must always be placed
   in parallel around whatever you're
   investigating (p.52) — NOT around any
   other bit of the circuit, e.g. the battery.

Measure **Potential Difference** and **Current** for **Different Lengths**

1) Attach a crocodile clip to the wire level with 0 cm on the ruler.
2) Attach the second crocodile clip to the wire a short distance from the first clip.
3) Write down the length of the wire between the clips.
4) Close the switch, then record the current through the wire and the pd across it.
5) Use $R = V \div I$ (from the equation $V = IR$ on p.42) to calculate the resistance of the wire.
6) Open the switch and move the second crocodile clip along the wire.
7) Repeat steps 3 to 6 for a range of wire lengths.

Plot a **Graph** of your **Results**

1) Plot a graph of resistance against wire length.
2) Draw a line of best fit through your points.
3) Your graph should be a straight line through the origin
   (where length and resistance are both zero).
4) This means resistance is directly proportional to length
   — the longer the wire, the greater the resistance.

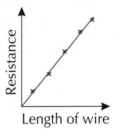

Be careful with the temperature of the wire...

If a large current flows through a wire, it can cause it to heat up (which will increase the resistance).
So use a low pd to stop it getting too hot and turn off the circuit between readings to let it cool.

I-V Characteristics

I-V characteristics tell you how the current through a component changes as the potential difference across it is increased. You need to know the I-V characteristics of ohmic conductors, filament lamps and diodes.

I-V Characteristics Show How Current Changes With Pd

1) An 'I-V characteristic' graph shows how the current (I) flowing through a component changes as the potential difference (V) across it changes.

2) Components with straight line I-V characteristics are called linear components (e.g. a fixed resistor).

3) Components with curved I-V characteristics are non-linear components (e.g. a filament lamp or a diode).

4) To find the resistance at any point on the I-V characteristic, first read off the values of I and V at that point. Then use $R = V \div I$ (from $V = IR$ on page 42).

Three Very Important I-V Characteristics

Make sure you know these graphs really well — you might be asked to sketch one in the exam.

Ohmic Conductor (e.g. resistor at a constant temperature)

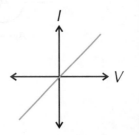

1) Current is directly proportional to potential difference.
2) So the graph of current against potential difference is a straight line.

Filament Lamp

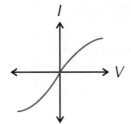

1) Temperature increases as current increases.
2) So resistance increases.
3) This makes it harder for current to flow.
4) So the graph gets less steep.

Diode

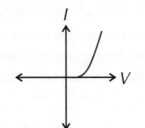

1) Current only flows in one direction.
2) The diode has very high resistance in the reverse direction.

You may be asked to interpret an I-V characteristic...

Make sure you take care when reading values off the graph. Pay close attention to the axes, and make sure you've converted all values to the correct units before you do any calculations.

PRACTICAL Investigating *I-V* Characteristics

On the previous page you met <u>*I-V* characteristics</u>. Now, here's all you need to know to set up a <u>practical</u> in order to collect data to draw some *I-V* characteristics of your very own.

You Can **Investigate** *I-V* Characteristics

You should do this experiment for <u>different components</u>, including a <u>filament lamp</u>, a <u>diode</u> and a <u>resistor at a fixed temperature</u>.

1) Set up the <u>test circuit</u> shown below.

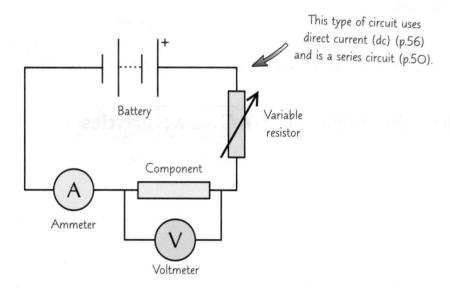

This type of circuit uses direct current (dc) (p.56) and is a series circuit (p.50).

Battery

Variable resistor

Component

Ammeter

Voltmeter

2) The <u>variable resistor</u> is used to <u>change</u> the <u>current</u> in the circuit. This changes the <u>potential difference</u> across the <u>component</u>.

3) Now you need to get <u>sets</u> of <u>current</u> and <u>potential difference</u> readings:
   - Set the <u>resistance</u> of the variable resistor.
   - Measure the <u>current through</u> and <u>potential difference across</u> the component.
   - Take measurements at a number of <u>different</u> resistances.

4) <u>Swap</u> over the wires connected to the cell to reverse the <u>direction of the current</u>. The ammeter should now display <u>negative readings</u>.

5) <u>Repeat</u> step 3 to get results for negative values of current.

6) Plot a <u>graph</u> with <u>current</u> on the *y*-axis and <u>potential difference</u> on the *x*-axis.

PRACTICAL TIP

Ammeters must be connected in series, voltmeters in parallel...

With any circuit, ammeters and voltmeters need to be connected correctly. <u>Ammeters</u> must be in <u>series</u> and <u>voltmeters</u> must be <u>parallel</u> to the component you're investigating (see p.44).

Warm-Up & Exam Questions

Phew — circuits aren't the easiest thing in the world, are they? Make sure you've understood the last few pages by trying these questions. If you get stuck, just go back and re-read the relevant page.

Warm-Up Questions

1) Draw the symbol for a light-emitting diode (LED).
2) What is an electric current?
3) What are the units of resistance?
4) Give an example of an ohmic conductor.
5) How should a voltmeter be connected in a circuit to measure the pd across a component?
6) What is an *I-V* characteristic?

Exam Questions

1   **Figure 1** shows a circuit diagram. The circuit's switch is closed for 2 minutes. While the switch is closed the ammeter reads 0.30 A. *Grade 3-4*

Figure 1

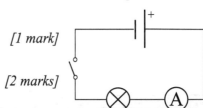

1.1   Write down the equation that links current, charge and time.

[1 mark]

1.2   Calculate the total charge that flows through the filament lamp.

[2 marks]

1.3   Use words from the box to complete the sentence.

ohmic	current	potential difference
non-linear	resistance	linear

A filament lamp is a _____ component. As the temperature
of the filament increases, the _____ of the lamp increases.

[2 marks]

2   A student wants to produce a graph of current against potential difference for component X. **Figure 2** shows an incomplete diagram of the circuit he is going to use. *Grade 4-5*

Figure 2

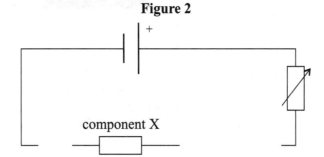

component X

2.1   Complete the circuit by adding an ammeter and a voltmeter.

[2 marks]

2.2   Predict the shape of the graph that the student will produce. Explain your answer.

[2 marks]

Circuit Devices

You might consider yourself a bit of an expert in <u>circuit components</u> — you're enlightened about bulbs, you're switched on to switches... Just make sure you know these ones as well — they're a bit trickier.

A **Light-Dependent Resistor** or "**LDR**"

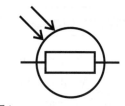

This is the circuit symbol for a light-dependent resistor.

1) The <u>resistance</u> of an LDR changes as the <u>intensity</u> of <u>light</u> changes.
2) In <u>bright light</u>, the resistance is <u>low</u>.
3) In <u>darkness</u>, the resistance is <u>high</u>.
4) LDRs have lots of <u>uses</u> including turning on lights when it gets <u>dark</u>.
5) This can be used in <u>automatic night lights</u>, or outdoor lighting.
6) They're also used in <u>burglar detectors</u>.

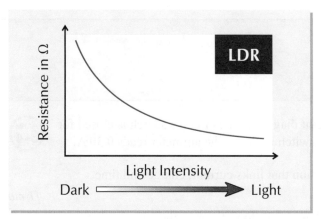

Thermistor Resistance Decreases as Temperature Increases

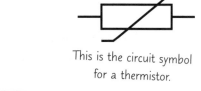

This is the circuit symbol for a thermistor.

1) A <u>thermistor</u> is a <u>temperature dependent</u> resistor.
2) In <u>hot</u> conditions, the resistance <u>drops</u>.
3) In <u>cool</u> conditions, the resistance goes <u>up</u>.
4) Thermistors are used in <u>car engines</u> and central heating <u>thermostats</u>.
5) <u>Thermostats</u> turn the heating <u>on</u> when it's <u>cool</u> and <u>off</u> when it's <u>warm</u>.

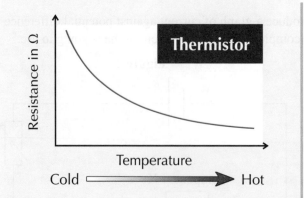

Thermistors and LDRs have many applications...

And they're not just limited to the examples on this page. Oh no. For example, LDRs are used in <u>digital cameras</u> to control how long the <u>shutter</u> should stay open for. If the <u>light level</u> is <u>low</u>, changes in the <u>resistance</u> cause the shutter to <u>stay open for longer</u> than if the light level was higher. How interesting.

Sensing Circuits

Now you've learnt about what <u>LDRs</u> and <u>thermistors</u> do, it's time to take a look at how they're put to use.

You Can Use Thermistors in **Sensing Circuits**

<u>Sensing circuits</u> can be used to automatically <u>change the pd</u> across components depending on changes in the <u>environment</u>.

1) The circuit on the right is a <u>sensing circuit</u> used to <u>control</u> a fan in a room.

2) The <u>potential difference</u> of the power supply is <u>shared out</u> between the thermistor and the fixed resistor (see p.50).

3) How much pd each one gets depends on their <u>resistances</u>.

4) The <u>larger</u> a component's resistance, the <u>more</u> of the pd it takes.

5) This circuit means that the pd across the fan <u>goes up</u> as the room <u>gets hotter</u>. Here's why:

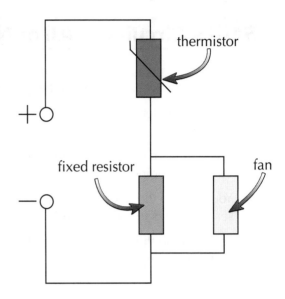

- As the room gets hotter, the resistance of the thermistor <u>decreases</u>.

- The thermistor takes a <u>smaller share</u> of the pd from the power supply.

- So the pd across the fixed resistor <u>rises</u>.

- The pd across the fixed resistor is <u>equal to</u> the pd across the <u>fan</u> (you'll see why on p.52).

- So the pd across the <u>fan</u> rises too, making the fan go <u>faster</u>.

6) If you connected the fan across the thermistor <u>instead</u>, the circuit would do the <u>opposite</u>.

7) The fan would <u>slow down</u> as the room got <u>hotter</u>.

You Can Also Use **LDRs** in **Sensing Circuits**

1) If you used an <u>LDR</u> instead of a thermistor in the circuit above it would be a <u>light sensing circuit</u>.

2) For example, the <u>bulb</u> in the sensing circuit on the right is connected <u>across the LDR</u>. This means it gets <u>brighter</u> as the room gets <u>darker</u>.

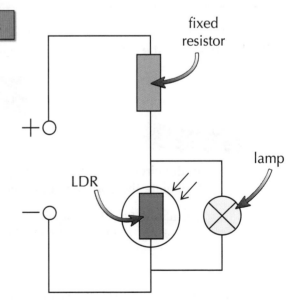

Sensing circuits react to changes in the surroundings...

<u>Sensing circuits</u> are a useful <u>application</u> of <u>thermistors</u> and <u>LDRs</u>, but they can be tricky to make sense of. They rely on the properties of <u>series</u> and <u>parallel circuits</u> — <u>read on</u> to learn all about them.

Series Circuits

You need to be able to tell if components are connected in series or parallel just by looking at circuit diagrams. You also need to know the rules about what happens with both types. Read on to find out more.

Series Circuits — All or Nothing

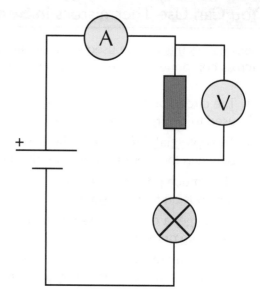

1) In series circuits, the components are all connected in a line between the ends of the power supply.

2) Only voltmeters break this rule. They're always in parallel (see p.52).

3) If you remove one component, the circuit is broken. So all the components stop working.

4) You can use the rules on this page and the next to design series circuits to measure and test all sorts of things.

5) For example the test circuit on p.46 and the sensing circuits on p.49.

Cell Potential Differences Add Up

1) There is a bigger potential difference when more cells are in series, provided the cells are all connected the same way.

2) For example when two batteries of voltage 1.5 V are connected in series they supply a total of 3 V.

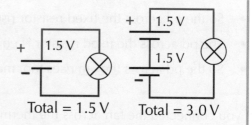

Potential Difference is Shared

1) In series circuits the total pd of the supply is shared between all of the components.

2) If you add up the pd across each component, you get the pd of the power supply.

$$V_{total} = V_1 + V_2 + ...$$

EXAMPLE:

In the circuit diagram on the right V_1 = 3.5 V.
Calculate the potential difference across the filament lamp, V_2.

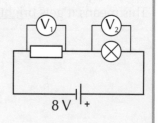

Substitute into the equation above, then rearrange for the unknown voltage.

$8 = 3.5 + V_2$
$V_2 = 8 - 3.5 = 4.5$ V

3) The bigger a component's resistance, the bigger its share of the total pd.

There are two main types of circuit — series and parallel...

Ammeters and voltmeters don't affect how you describe a circuit — you can have a parallel circuit (p.52) with ammeters connected in series, or a series circuit with voltmeters connected in parallel with components.

Series Circuits

We're not done with <u>series circuits</u> yet. Here's the low-down on <u>current</u> and <u>resistance</u>...

Current is the **Same Everywhere**

In series circuits the <u>same current</u> flows through <u>all components</u>.

$$I_1 = I_2 = ...$$

Resistance **Adds Up**

1) In series circuits, the <u>total resistance</u> of two components is found by <u>adding up</u> their resistances.

2) R_{total} is the <u>total resistance</u> of the circuit.
   R_1 and R_2 are resistances of the <u>components</u>:

$$R_{total} = R_1 + R_2$$

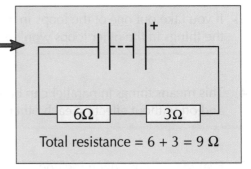

Total resistance = 6 + 3 = 9 Ω

EXAMPLE:

For the circuit diagram on the right, calculate the current passing through the circuit.

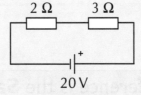

20 V

1) First find the <u>total resistance</u> by <u>adding together</u> the resistance of the two resistors.

$R_{total} = 2 + 3 = 5$ Ω

2) Then <u>rearrange</u> $V = IR$ for I.

3) <u>Substitute</u> in the values you have and calculate the current.

$I = V \div R$
$= 20 \div 5$
$= 4$ A

3) You need to be able to <u>explain</u> why adding resistors <u>in series</u> increases the total resistance of the circuit:

- Adding a resistor in <u>series</u> means the resistors have to <u>share</u> the total pd.
- This means the pd across each resistor is <u>lower</u>, so the <u>current</u> through each resistor is lower ($V = IR$).
- The current is the <u>same everywhere</u>.
- So the <u>total current</u> in the circuit is <u>reduced</u> when a resistor is added.
- This means the total <u>resistance</u> of the circuit has <u>gone up</u>.

Series circuits aren't used very much in the real world...

Since series circuits put <u>all</u> components on the <u>same loop of wire</u>, and the current is the same through each component, if one <u>component breaks</u> it'll <u>break the circuit</u>, and all other components will <u>stop working</u> too. Parallel circuits are much more useful and can avoid this problem — as you're about to find out...

Parallel Circuits

Parallel circuits can be a little bit trickier to wrap your head around, but they're much more useful than series circuits. Most electronics use a combination of series and parallel circuitry.

Parallel Circuits — Every **Component** Connected **Separately**

1) In parallel circuits, each component is separately connected to the ends of the power supply.

2) Only ammeters break this rule, they're always in series (see p.50).

3) If you take out one of the loops in a parallel circuit, the things in the other loops won't be affected.

4) This means things in parallel can be switched on and off without affecting each other.

5) Everyday circuits often include a mixture of series and parallel parts.

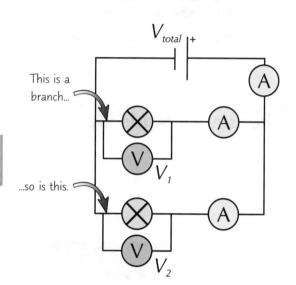

This is a branch...

...so is this.

V_{total}

V_1

V_2

Potential Difference is the **Same** Across All **Components**

1) In parallel circuits all components get the full source pd.

2) So the potential difference is the same across all components.

$$V_1 = V_2 = V_3 = ...$$

3) This means that identical bulbs connected in parallel will all be at the same brightness.

Parallel circuits have a big advantage over series circuits...

If a component in a parallel circuit breaks, only that component's branch will be affected. Current will continue to flow through all of the circuit's other branches. A classic example of this is fairy lights. If a bulb breaks, only the broken bulb will go out, since they're wired in parallel.

Parallel Circuits

In some ways current in a circuit is a little like water flowing in a river. And, just as like flowing water splits when it reaches a fork in the river, <u>current</u> will split <u>when</u> it reaches a <u>branch</u> in the circuit.

Current is **Shared** Between Branches

1) In parallel circuits the <u>total current</u> in a circuit is equal to the <u>sum</u> of all the currents through the <u>separate components</u>.

2) At <u>junctions</u>, the current either <u>splits</u> or <u>rejoins</u>.

3) The total current going <u>into</u> a junction must equal the total current <u>leaving</u> it.

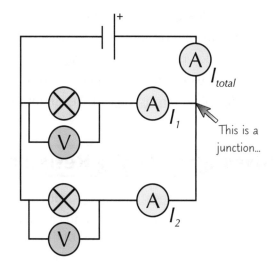

This is a junction...

$$I_{total} = I_1 + I_2 + ...$$

EXAMPLE:

For the circuit diagram on the right, find the pd measured by V_1 and the current measured by A_3.

1) The resistors are in <u>parallel</u>, so the pd across each resistor is the <u>same</u> as the <u>cell pd</u>.

2) The current <u>into</u> the first junction is the <u>same</u> as the current <u>out</u> of it.

Cell pd = 6 V
V_1 = 6 V

In: 2 A   Out: 1 A + A_3
So A_3 = 2 − 1 = 1 A

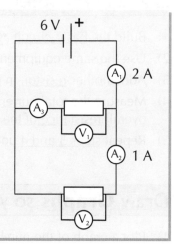

Adding a Resistor in Parallel **Reduces** the **Total Resistance**

The total resistance of <u>two resistors connected in parallel</u> is <u>less than</u> the resistance of the <u>smallest</u> of the two resistors. Here's why:

1) If you add a resistor in parallel, both resistors still have the <u>same potential difference</u> across them as the power supply.

2) This means the 'pushing force' making the current flow is still the <u>same</u>.

3) But by adding another loop, the <u>current</u> has <u>more than one</u> direction to go in.

4) More <u>current</u> can flow around the circuit, so the total current <u>increases</u>.

5) This means the <u>total resistance</u> of the circuit is <u>lower</u> (as $R = V \div I$).

 **PRACTICAL** **Investigating Circuits**

You saw on page 44 how the length of the wire used in a circuit affects its resistance. Now it's time to do an experiment to see how placing resistors in series or in parallel can affect the resistance of the whole circuit.

First Set Up the **Basic Circuit**

1) Find at least four identical resistors.
2) Build the circuit shown on the right.
3) Write down the pd of the battery. This is the pd of the circuit (V).
4) Read the current in the circuit (I) from the ammeter.
5) Calculate the resistance of the circuit using $R = V \div I$.

Investigate Adding **Resistors in Series**...

1) Add another resistor, in series with the first.
2) Measure the current again and calculate resistance again. The pd is the same as the pd of the battery.
3) Repeat steps 1 and 2 until you've added all of your resistors.

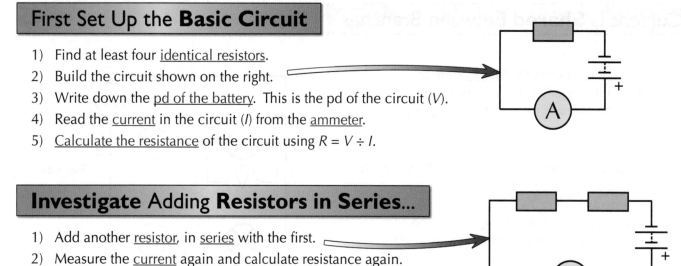

... and in **Parallel**

1) Build the basic circuit again. You already know its resistance.
2) Use the same equipment so it's a fair test.
3) Add another resistor, in parallel with the first.
4) Measure the total current through the circuit and calculate the overall resistance of the circuit. The pd is still the same as before.
5) Repeat steps 3 and 4 until you've added all of your resistors.

Draw **Graphs** so you can **Compare** your Results

1) Plot a graph of the number of resistors in the circuit against the total resistance.
2) You should get graphs that look like this:

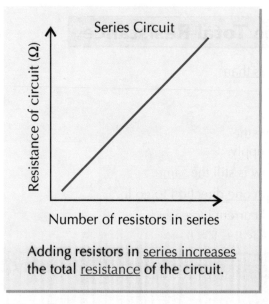

Adding resistors in series increases the total resistance of the circuit.

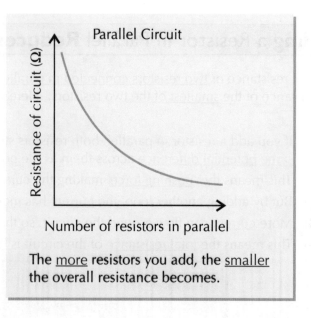

The more resistors you add, the smaller the overall resistance becomes.

Warm-Up & Exam Questions

Time to check and see what you can remember about those circuit devices, plus parallel and series circuits.

Warm-Up Questions

1) Give one use of a light-dependent resistor (LDR).
2) What happens to the resistance of a thermistor as its temperature increases?
3) Describe what a series circuit is.
4) True or false? In a series circuit, if you add up the pd across each component, you get the pd of the power supply.
5) How do you work out the total resistance in a series circuit?
6) Which has the higher total resistance: two resistors in series, or the same two resistors in parallel?

Exam Questions

1   Which of the following statements does **not** apply to parallel circuits? Tick **one** box. *(Grade 3-4)*

If one branch is disconnected, the other branches will not be affected. ☐

Total resistance is equal to the sum of the individual resistances. ☐

Current splits when it reaches a junction. ☐

Each branch experiences the whole supply pd. ☐

[1 mark]

2   **Figure 1** shows a series circuit. *(Grade 3-4)*

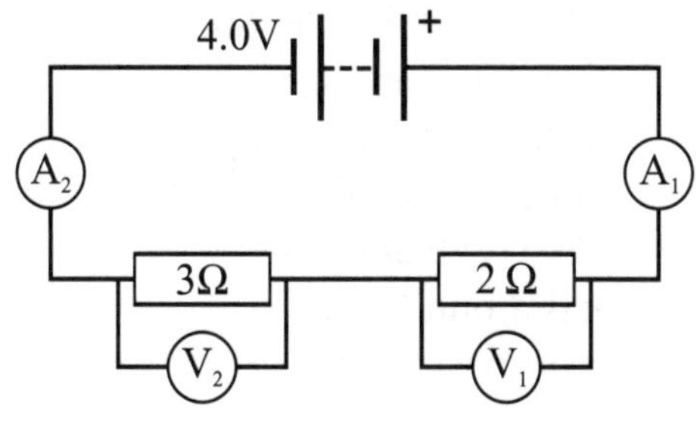

2.1   Calculate the total resistance in the circuit.

[2 marks]

2.2   The current through A_1 is 0.4 A.
What is the current through A_2? Explain your answer.

[2 marks]

2.3 V_1 reads 1.6 V.
Calculate the reading on V_2.

[2 marks]

Figure 1

3   **Figure 2** shows a circuit that contains an LED, a light-dependent resistor and a cell. *(Grade 4-5)*

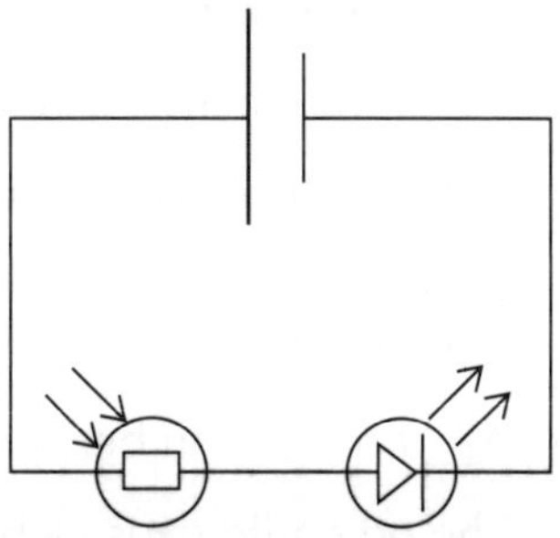

3.1   Describe how you could tell that a current is flowing in the circuit.

[1 mark]

3.2   The circuit is placed in a well lit room. At the end of the day, the lights in the room are turned off. Describe and explain how the resistance of the circuit changes when the room lights are switched off.

[2 marks]

Figure 2

Electricity in the Home

Now you've learnt the basics of electrical circuits, it's time to see how electricity is used in everyday life.

Mains Supply is ac, Battery Supply is dc

1) An alternating potential difference is a potential difference that is constantly changing direction. It produces an alternating current (ac).

2) In an alternating current, the current (flow of charge) is also constantly changing direction.

3) The UK mains supply (the electricity in your home) is an ac supply at around 230 V.

4) The frequency (p.110) of the ac mains supply is 50 Hz (hertz).

5) Direct current (dc) is a current that is always flowing in the same direction.

6) It's created by a direct potential difference. The direction of a direct potential difference is always the same.

Cells and batteries supply dc.

Most Cables Have Three Separate Wires

1) Most electrical appliances are connected to the mains supply by three-core cables.

2) They have three wires covered with plastic insulation inside them.

3) They are coloured so that it is easy to tell the different wires apart.

LIVE WIRE — brown.
1) The live wire provides the alternating potential difference from the mains supply.
2) It is at about 230 V.

NEUTRAL WIRE — blue.
1) The neutral wire completes the circuit.
2) When the appliance is operating normally, current flows through the live and neutral wires.
3) It is around 0 V.

EARTH WIRE — green and yellow.
1) The earth wire is a safety wire.
2) It stops the appliance becoming live:
   - It is connected to the metal casing of an appliance.
   - If a fault causes the live wire to touch the casing, the current flows away through the earth wire.
3) It's also at 0 V.

The Live Wire Can Give You an Electric Shock

1) There is a pd between the live wire and your body (which is at 0 V).

2) Touching the live wire can cause a current to flow through your body.

3) This can give you a dangerous electric shock.

4) Even if a switch is turned off (the switch is open), touching the live wire is still dangerous. This is because it still has a pd of 230 V.

5) Any connection between live and earth can be dangerous.

6) The pd could cause a huge current to flow, which could result in a fire.

Power of Electrical Appliances

Energy is transferred between stores electrically (like you saw on page 19) by electrical appliances.

Energy is Transferred from Cells and Other Sources

1) When a charge moves around a circuit, work is done against the resistance of the circuit.
2) Whenever work is done, energy is transferred.
3) When the work is done by a charge, the energy is transferred electrically.
4) Electrical appliances transfer energy to components in the circuit when a current flows.

Kettles transfer energy electrically from the mains supply to the thermal energy store of the heating element inside the kettle.

Energy is transferred electrically from the battery of a handheld fan to the kinetic energy store of the fan's motor.

Energy Transferred Depends on the Power

1) The total energy transferred by an appliance depends on how long the appliance is on for and its power.
2) The power of an appliance is the energy that it transfers per second.
3) So the more energy it transfers in a given time, the higher its power.
4) The amount of energy transferred by electrical work is given by:

This equation should be familiar from page 28.

$$\text{Energy transferred (J)} = \text{Power (W)} \times \text{Time (s)} \qquad E = Pt$$

 **EXAMPLE:**

A 600 W microwave is used for 5 minutes. How much energy does it transfer?

1) Convert the time into seconds. $\qquad t = 5 \times 60 = 300 \text{ s}$
2) Substitute the numbers into $E = Pt$ $\qquad E = Pt = 600 \times 300$
   to find the energy transferred. $\qquad = 180\ 000 \text{ J}$

5) Appliances are often given a power rating. This is the power that they work at.
6) The power rating tells you how much energy is transferred between stores when the appliance is used.
7) An appliance with a higher power will cost more to run for a given time, as it uses more energy.

A 850 W microwave will transfer more energy between stores during 5 minutes than the 600 W microwave in the example above. This means it will cost more to use it for 5 minutes.

Power is measured in watts, W — one W is equal to one J/s...

Remember, the power rating of an electrical appliance is the amount of energy transferred to the appliance per second, not the amount that it transfers to useful energy stores.

More on Power

And we're not done yet. There are even more <u>power equations</u> for you to get your head around. How fun.

Potential Difference is **Energy Transferred** per **Charge Passed**

1) As a charge moves around a circuit, <u>energy</u> is transferred <u>to</u> or <u>from</u> it.
2) The <u>energy transferred</u> by a component depends on the <u>potential difference</u> across it and the <u>charge flowing</u> through it.
3) The <u>formula</u> is really simple:

| Energy transferred (J) = Charge Flow (C) × Potential Difference (V) | $E = QV$ |

An electric toothbrush contains a 3.0 V battery. 140 C of charge passes through the toothbrush as it is used. Calculate the energy transferred.

<u>Substitute</u> the numbers into $E = QV$ to find the <u>energy transferred</u>.

$E = QV = 140 \times 3.0 = 420$ J

Power Also Depends on **Current** and **Potential Difference**

1) You saw on the previous page that power is <u>energy transferred</u> in a given <u>time</u>.
2) The <u>power</u> of an appliance can also be found using:

| Power (W) = Potential difference (V) × Current (A) | $P = VI$ |

Resistance (Ω)

3) You can also find the power if you <u>don't know</u> the <u>potential difference</u>, using: $P = I^2R$

A motor with a power of 1250 W has a resistance of 50 Ω. Calculate the current flowing through the motor.

1) First <u>rearrange</u> the formula $P = I^2R$ to make I the subject.
   • <u>Divide</u> both sides by R.
   • Find the <u>square root</u> of both sides.
2) Now just <u>plug in</u> the numbers.

$P \div R = I^2$ so $I^2 = P \div R$

$I = \sqrt{P \div R}$

$I = \sqrt{1250 \div 50} = \sqrt{25}$
$= 5$ A

Your calculator should have a '√' (square root) button to help with these calculations.

National Grid

The national grid is a giant web of wires that covers the whole of Britain, getting electricity from power stations to homes everywhere. Whoever you pay for your electricity, it's the national grid that gets it to you.

Electricity is Distributed via the National Grid

1) The national grid is a giant system of cables and transformers that covers the UK.

2) It transfers electrical power from power stations to consumers (anyone who is using electricity) across the UK.

Electricity Production has to Meet Demand

1) Throughout the day, the amount of electricity used (the demand) changes.

2) Power stations have to produce enough electricity for everyone to have it when they need it.

3) More electricity is used when people get up in the morning, come home from school or work and when it starts to get dark or cold outside.

4) Power stations often run at well below their maximum power output, so that they can increase their power if needed.

5) This means that the national grid can cope with a high demand, even if another station shuts down without warning.

Energy demands are ever increasing...

The national grid has been working since the 1930s and has gone through many changes and updates since then to meet increasing energy demands. Using energy-efficient appliances and switching unneeded lights off are some ways we might ensure that supply and demand stay in balance. It'll do wonders for the electricity bill too, so it's worth bearing in mind.

National Grid

To transfer electricity <u>efficiently</u>, the national grid makes use of some clever tech called <u>transformers</u>.

The National Grid Uses a **High Pd** and a **Low Current**

1) The national grid transfers <u>loads</u> of energy, so the <u>power</u> has to be <u>very high</u>.

2) To transmit this <u>huge</u> amount of <u>power</u> you need either a <u>high potential difference</u> or a <u>high current</u>.

3) This is because <u>*P = VI*</u> (from page 58).

4) A <u>high current</u> means <u>loads of energy</u> is lost to thermal energy stores as the wires <u>heat up</u>.

5) So the national grid transmits electricity at a very <u>high pd</u>.
For a <u>given power</u>, the higher the pd the <u>lower the current</u>.

6) This <u>reduces the energy lost</u>, making the national grid an <u>efficient</u> way of transferring energy.

Potential Difference is Changed by **Transformers**

1) <u>Step-up transformers</u> are used to <u>increase the pd</u> from <u>power stations</u> to electric <u>cables</u>.
2) <u>Step-down transformers</u> bring the pd <u>back down</u> to <u>safe levels</u> before the electricity gets to <u>homes</u>.

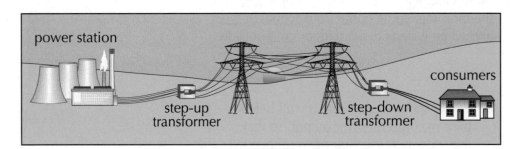

3) Transformers all have two coils, a <u>primary coil</u> and a <u>secondary coil</u>, joined with an <u>iron core</u>.
4) The <u>power</u> of a primary coil is given by <u>power = pd × current</u>.
5) The <u>power in primary coil = power in secondary coil</u>, so:

$$\text{pd across primary coil (V)} \times \text{current in primary coil (A)} = \text{pd across secondary coil (V)} \times \text{current in secondary coil (A)}$$

The national grid — it's a powerful thing...

The key to the <u>efficiency</u> of the <u>national grid</u> is the power equation, <u>*P = VI*</u> (see page 58). If you have a <u>constant</u> power, but <u>increase</u> the potential difference using a transformer, the current must <u>decrease</u>. Having as <u>low</u> a <u>current</u> as possible makes sure that power is transferred as <u>efficiently</u> as possible.

Warm-Up & Exam Questions

Who knew there was so much to learn about electricity in the home and across the country?
See if it's switched on a light bulb in your brain by trying out these questions.

Warm-Up Questions

1) Name the three wires in a three-core cable that connect electrical appliances to the mains supply.
2) What is the main energy transfer when electric current flows through an electric kettle?
3) What is the equation linking power, current and resistance?
4) What is the national grid?

Exam Questions

1 This question is about the national grid.

1.1 Use words from the box to complete the sentence.

current	potential difference	step-up	step-down

_____ transformers are used between the power station and the transmission cables.
This increases the _____ , so that power may be transferred more efficiently.

[2 marks]

1.2 Which describes the UK mains electricity supply? Tick **one** box.

☐ 230 V ac   ☐ 170 V ac   ☐ 230 V dc   ☐ 170 V dc

[1 mark]

2 **Table 1** shows the power and potential difference ratings for two kettles.

Table 1

	Power (W)	Potential Difference (V)
Kettle A	2760	230
Kettle B	3000	230

2.1 Write down the equation linking power, potential difference and current.

[1 mark]

2.2 Calculate the current, in amps, drawn from the mains supply by kettle A.

[2 marks]

2.3 A student wants to test which kettle heats water most quickly. He measures the increase in water temperature in each kettle after 1 minute. Identify one variable the student must control.

[1 mark]

2.4 The kettles are equally efficient.
A second student states: 'Kettle B has the greatest power so it will heat water most quickly.'
Justify the student's statement.

[2 marks]

Revision Summary for Topic 2

That wraps up <u>Topic 2</u> — time to put yourself to the test and find out <u>how much you really know</u>.
- Try these questions and <u>tick off each one</u> when you <u>get it right</u>.
- When you've done <u>all the questions</u> under a heading and are <u>completely happy</u> with it, tick it off.

Circuit Basics (p.41-46) ☑
1) Draw the circuit diagram symbols for a resistor, a voltmeter, an LED and a diode. ☑
2) Why does a circuit need a source of potential difference? ☑
3) What are the units of charge and current? ☑
4) What is the equation that links potential difference, current and resistance? ☑
5) What is an ohmic conductor? ☑
6) Describe how you would investigate how the length of a wire affects its resistance. ☑
7) Name one linear component and one non-linear component. ☑
8) Sketch the *I-V* characteristic of a diode. ☑
9) Draw a circuit that could be used to investigate the *I-V* characteristic of a filament lamp. ☑

Circuit Devices and Types of Circuit (p.48-54) ☑
10) How does the resistance of an LDR change as light intensity increases? ☑
11) What happens to the resistance of a thermistor as it gets colder? ☑
12) True or false? Potential difference is shared between components in a series circuit. ☑
13) True or false? The current is the same at all points in a series circuit. ☑
14) True or false? The potential difference across each component connected in parallel is different. ☑
15) A circuit consists of a battery and a resistor. How does the overall resistance
    of the circuit change when a second resistor is added in parallel? ☑
16) Describe an experiment to investigate how adding resistors in series and parallel affects the total
    resistance of the circuit. ☑
17) Explain why adding resistors in parallel decreases the total resistance of a circuit,
    but adding them in series increases the total resistance. ☑

Electricity in the Home (p.56) ☑
18) True or false? Mains supply electricity is an alternating current. ☑
19) What is the potential difference and the frequency of the UK mains supply? ☑
20) Name and give the colours of the three wires in a three-core cable. ☑
21) Give the potential differences for the three wires in a three-core mains cable. ☑
22) Explain why touching a live wire is dangerous. ☑

Power and the National Grid (p.57-60) ☑
23) Describe the useful energy transfer that occurs for a battery-powered fan. ☑
24) State three equations that can be used to calculate electrical power. ☑
25) What is the power rating of an appliance? ☑
26) Explain why electricity is transferred by the national grid at a high pd but low current. ☑
27) How are step-up and step-down transformers used in the national grid? ☑

Particle Model

Everything is made up of <u>small particles</u>. The particle model <u>describes</u> how these particles behave.

There are **Three States of Matter**

1) The <u>three states of matter</u> are <u>solid</u> (e.g. ice), <u>liquid</u> (e.g. water) and <u>gas</u> (e.g. water vapour).
2) The <u>particle model</u> explains the <u>differences</u> between the <u>states of matter</u>:
   - The <u>particles</u> of a <u>certain material</u> are <u>always</u> the <u>same</u>, no matter what <u>state</u> it is in.
   - But the particles have different <u>amounts of energy</u> in different states.
   - And the <u>forces</u> between particles are <u>different</u> in each state.
   - This means that the particles are <u>arranged</u> (laid out) <u>differently</u> in different states.

Solids

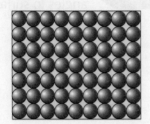

1) Particles are held <u>close together</u> by <u>strong forces</u> in a <u>regular, fixed pattern</u>.
2) The particles don't have <u>much energy</u>.
3) So they can only <u>vibrate</u> (jiggle about) around a <u>fixed position</u>.

Liquids

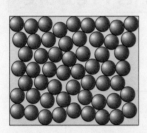

1) The particles are held <u>close together</u> in an <u>irregular pattern</u>.
2) The particles have <u>more energy</u> than the particles in a solid.
3) They can <u>move past</u> each other in <u>random directions</u> at <u>low speeds</u>.

Gases

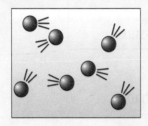

1) The particles <u>aren't</u> held close together. There are <u>no forces</u> between them.
2) The particles have <u>more energy</u> than in liquids and solids.
3) The particles <u>constantly move</u> around in <u>random directions</u> at a <u>range of speeds</u>.

The more energy in their kinetic stores, the faster the particles move...

Learn those diagrams above and make sure that you can describe the <u>arrangement</u> and <u>movement</u> of particles in solids, liquids and gases. You should also be able to talk about how much <u>energy</u> they have.

Particle Motion in Gases

The particle model explains how temperature, pressure and energy in kinetic stores are all related. And this page is here to explain it all to you. I bet you're just itching to find out more...

Gas Particles **Bump into Things** and Create **Pressure**

1) Particles in a gas are free to move around.

2) They collide with (bump into) each other and the sides of the container they're in.

3) When they hit something, they apply a force to it. Pressure is the force applied over a given area.

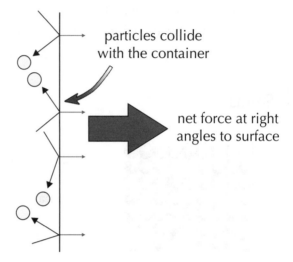

particles collide with the container

net force at right angles to surface

Increasing the **Temperature** of a Gas Increases its **Pressure**

1) The temperature of a gas depends on the average energy in the kinetic energy stores of the gas particles.

- The hotter the gas, the higher the average energy.

- If particles have more energy in their kinetic stores, they move faster.

- So the hotter the gas, the faster the particles move on average.

- Faster particles hit the sides of the container more often. This increases the force on the container.

So increasing the temperature of a gas increases its pressure.

2) This only works if the space the gas takes up (the volume) doesn't change.

Higher temperatures mean higher average energies in kinetic stores...

The particle model can be used to explain what happens when you change the temperature of a gas which is kept at a constant volume. Have a look back on page 63 for more about the particle model.

Density of Materials

The <u>density</u> of an object tells you how many of its <u>particles</u> are squished into a <u>given space</u>.

The **Particle Model** can also Explain **Density**

1) <u>Density</u> is a measure of <u>how much mass</u> there is in a <u>certain space</u>.
2) You can work out density using:

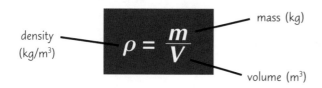

density (kg/m³) $\rho = \dfrac{m}{V}$ mass (kg)

volume (m³)

$$\frac{m}{\rho \times V}$$

> **EXAMPLE:**
>
> **A 0.0020 m³ block of aluminium has a mass of 5.4 kg. Calculate the density of aluminium.**
>
> density = mass ÷ volume
> = 5.4 ÷ 0.0020
> = 2700 kg/m³

3) The density of an object depends on <u>what it's made of</u> and how its <u>particles</u> are <u>arranged</u>.
4) A <u>dense</u> material has its particles <u>packed tightly</u> together.
5) So, <u>solids</u> are generally <u>denser</u> than <u>liquids</u>.
6) And <u>liquids</u> are generally <u>denser</u> than <u>gases</u>.

You Can Find the **Density** of a **Regularly Shaped Object**

PRACTICAL

1) Use a <u>balance</u> to measure its <u>mass</u> (see p.134).
2) Measure its <u>length</u>, <u>width</u> and <u>height</u> with a <u>ruler</u>.
3) Then calculate its <u>volume</u> using the <u>formula</u> for that shape.
4) Use <u>density = mass ÷ volume</u> to find the density.

The volume of a cuboid is equal to length × width × height.

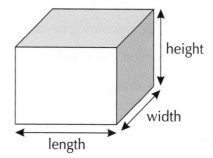

height

width

length

WORKING SCIENTIFICALLY

The denser the substance, the closer together its particles are...

When you're measuring the <u>dimensions</u> of an object, think about which apparatus is best to use. If what you're measuring is pretty <u>small</u>, a <u>ruler</u> won't give you very <u>accurate</u> measurements. For small measurements, a <u>micrometer</u> or <u>Vernier callipers</u> would be more appropriate.

You need to be able to carry out practicals to work out the <u>densities</u> of different <u>solids</u> and <u>liquids</u>.

Find the Density of an **Irregularly Shaped Object** Using a **Eureka Can**

1) Use a <u>balance</u> to measure the object's <u>mass</u>.

2) <u>Fill</u> a <u>eureka can</u> (a can with a spout in its side) with water.

3) The <u>water level</u> should end up <u>just below</u> the start of the spout.

4) Place a <u>measuring cylinder</u> (p.133) under the end of the spout.

5) Place your object <u>into the water</u>.
   This will <u>push</u> some of the water <u>out</u> through the spout.

There's more about eureka cans on page 133.

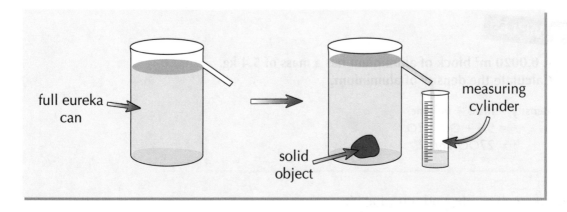

full eureka can

measuring cylinder

solid object

6) <u>Measure the volume</u> of water that has collected in the measuring cylinder.

7) This is <u>equal to</u> the <u>volume</u> of the <u>object</u>.

8) Use the <u>formula</u> on the previous page to find the object's <u>density</u>.

For both of these experiments, you'll need to know that 1 ml = 1 cm³ and that 1 cm³ = 0.000001 m³.

Find the Density of a **Liquid** Using a **Measuring Cylinder**

1) Place a <u>measuring cylinder</u> on a balance and <u>zero</u> the balance (p.134).

2) Pour <u>50 ml</u> of the liquid into the measuring cylinder.

3) Record the liquid's <u>mass</u> shown on the mass balance.

4) Use the <u>formula</u> on the previous page to find the <u>density</u>.
   The <u>volume</u> is <u>50 cm³</u>, or <u>0.00005 m³</u>.

46.568

PRACTICAL TIP

A eureka can makes it pretty easy to find an object's volume...

Try not to put your fingers in the water as you're dropping your object into the eureka can.
This will displace <u>more water</u>, and make your volume measurement <u>too big</u>. You could always
hang your object from a piece of <u>thread</u> and lower it in if you want to be extra careful.

Internal Energy and Changes of State

This page is all about heating things. Take a look at your <u>specific heat capacity</u> notes (p.23) before you start. You need to understand it and be able to use $\Delta E = mc\Delta\theta$ for this topic too I'm afraid.

Internal Energy is the Total Energy Stored by Particles in a System

1) The <u>energy stored</u> in a <u>system</u> (p.19) is stored by its <u>particles</u> (atoms and molecules).
2) The particles have energy in their <u>kinetic energy stores</u>.
3) They also have energy in their <u>potential energy stores</u> because of their <u>positions</u>.
4) The <u>internal energy</u> of a system is the <u>total energy</u> that all its particles have in their <u>kinetic</u> and <u>potential</u> energy stores.

Heating Increases Internal Energy

1) <u>Heating</u> a system <u>transfers</u> energy to its particles.
2) This increases the system's <u>internal energy</u>.
3) This leads to a <u>change in temperature</u> or a <u>change of state</u> (e.g. melting or boiling).
4) How much the temperature changes depends on the <u>mass</u> of the system, its <u>specific heat capacity</u> (p.23) and how much <u>energy</u> is transferred to it.
5) You can see this from the <u>equation</u> $\Delta E = mc\Delta\theta$.
6) A <u>change of state</u> happens when the particles have enough energy in their <u>kinetic energy stores</u> to <u>break the bonds</u> holding them together.

Mass Doesn't Change in a Change of State

1) A <u>change of state</u> can happen because of <u>cooling</u>, as well as heating.
2) The <u>changes of state</u> are:

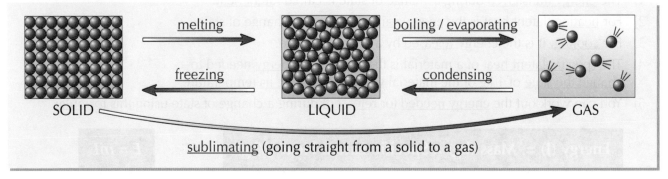

3) A <u>change of state</u> is a <u>physical</u> change (not a chemical change).
4) This means you <u>don't</u> end up with a <u>new material</u>.
5) The particles are just arranged in a <u>different way</u> (p.63).
6) The <u>number of particles</u> stays the same when the state changes.
7) This means the <u>mass is conserved</u> (it <u>doesn't change</u>).
8) If you <u>reverse</u> a change of state, the material will <u>get back</u> all the properties it had <u>before</u> the change.

Physical changes are different from chemical changes...

You should make sure you know all the <u>changes of state</u>, and why they are <u>physical changes</u>.

Specific Latent Heat

The <u>energy needed</u> to change the state of a substance is called <u>latent heat</u>. This is exciting stuff I tell you...

Temperature Doesn't Change During a Change of State

1) <u>Heating</u> a material <u>transfers energy</u> to the material.
2) This either increases the <u>temperature</u> of the material or changes its <u>state</u> (p.67).
3) During a <u>change of state</u>, the temperature <u>doesn't change</u>. But the <u>internal energy</u> does.
4) The energy transferred is used to <u>break bonds</u> between particles. It is <u>not</u> used to raise the temperature.

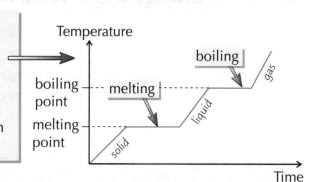

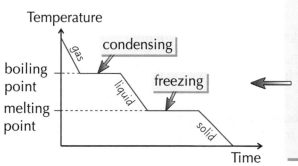

5) When a material <u>cools</u>, energy is <u>transferred away</u> from it.
6) As a material <u>condenses</u> or <u>freezes</u>, <u>bonds form</u> between particles. This causes <u>energy</u> to be <u>released</u>.
7) So its <u>internal energy decreases</u>, but its temperature <u>stays the same</u> during the change of state.
8) The <u>flat spots</u> on these graphs show that the <u>temperature doesn't change</u> during a change of state.

Specific Latent Heat is the Energy Needed to Change State

1) The <u>energy transferred</u> during a change of state is called <u>latent heat</u>.
2) For <u>heating</u>, latent heat is the <u>energy gained</u> to cause a change of state.
3) For <u>cooling</u>, it is the energy <u>released</u> by a change in state.
4) The <u>specific latent heat</u> of a material is the <u>amount of energy</u> needed to <u>change the state</u> of <u>1 kg</u> of the material <u>without changing its temperature</u>.
5) You can work out the <u>energy needed</u> (or <u>released</u>) during a change of state using this <u>formula</u>:

> **Energy (J) = Mass (kg) × Specific Latent Heat (J/kg)**   or: $E = mL$

6) Specific latent heat has <u>different names</u> for different changes of state:
7) For changing between a <u>solid</u> and a <u>liquid</u> it is called the <u>specific latent heat of fusion</u>.
8) For changing between a <u>liquid</u> and a <u>gas</u> it is called the <u>specific latent heat of vaporisation</u>.

The specific latent heat of vaporisation for water is 2 260 000 J/kg. How much energy is needed to completely boil 1.50 kg of water once it has reached its boiling point?

1) The mass and specific latent heat are in the <u>right units</u>, so just put them into the <u>formula</u>.
2) The units for the answer are <u>joules</u> because it's <u>energy</u>.

$E = mL$
$= 1.50 \times 2\ 260\ 000$
$= 3\ 390\ 000$ J

Warm-Up & Exam Questions

So that's it, you've covered everything from the particle model to changes of state. Once you think you've got to grips with the stuff in this topic, it's time to test yourself with these questions.

Warm-Up Questions

1) Describe the spacing and arrangement of particles in a solid.
2) What is density?
3) What happens to the internal energy of a system when it is heated?
4) What is the specific latent heat of vaporisation?
5) What are the units of specific latent heat?

Exam Questions

1 Use words in the box to complete the sentence below. *(Grade 1-3)*

| solid | condensation | evaporation | gas | sublimation |

If a liquid is heated to a certain temperature it starts to boil and turns into a ....

Another process that causes this change of state is ....

[2 marks]

2 A student has a collection of metal toy soldiers of different sizes made from the same metal. *(Grade 3-4)*

2.1 Which of the following statements is true? Tick **one** box.

☐ The masses and densities of each of the toy soldiers are the same.

☐ The masses of each of the toy soldiers are the same, but their densities may vary.

☐ The densities of each of the toy soldiers are the same, but their masses may vary.

[1 mark]

2.2 One of the soldiers has a mass of 200 g and a volume of 2.5×10^{-5} m^3.

The equation below can be used to calculate density.

density = mass ÷ volume

Calculate the density of the soldier.

[2 marks]

3 0.40 kg of liquid methanol is at its boiling point. *(Grade 3-4)*
The specific latent heat of vaporisation of methanol is 1200 J/kg.

Calculate the amount of energy needed to convert the liquid methanol to gaseous methanol.
Use the correct equation from the Physics Equation Sheet on the inside back cover.

[2 marks]

Topic 3 — Particle Model of Matter

Exam Questions

4 A student wants to measure the density of a pendant. **PRACTICAL**
He can use the equipment shown in **Figure 1**.

Figure 1

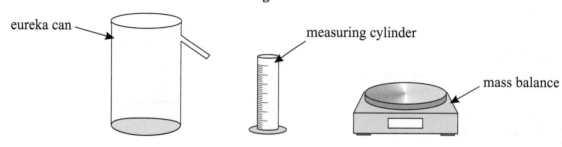

eureka can

measuring cylinder

mass balance

4.1 Name the **two** quantities the student should measure.

[2 marks]

4.2 Describe the steps the student could take to find the density of the pendant
with the equipment shown.

[5 marks]

5 The graph in **Figure 2** shows
the temperature of a substance
against time as it is heated.

Figure 2

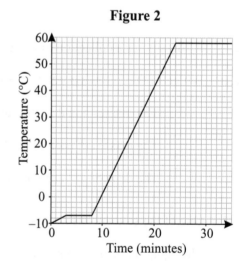

5.1 Describe what is happening during the period between
3 and 8 minutes from the beginning of heating.

[1 mark]

5.2 Give the melting and boiling points of the substance.

[2 marks]

6* A gas is sealed in a rigid container.
A scientist heats the container.

Figure 3

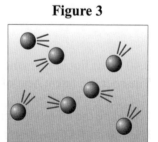

Figure 3 shows gas particles as represented in the particle model.
Use the particle model to explain why the pressure
of the gas increases as the container is heated.
In your answer, you should include a description of
how gas particles create pressure in the container.

[6 marks]

Revision Summary for Topic 3

Don't let all that stuff about gas pressures in <u>Topic 3</u> put too much pressure on you.
Try these questions to see whether you've really got to grips with <u>states of matter</u> and the <u>particle model</u>.

- Try these questions and <u>tick off each one</u> when you <u>get it right</u>.
- When you've done <u>all the questions</u> under a heading, and are <u>completely happy</u> with it, tick it off.

The Particle Model and Motion in Gases (p.63-64) ☑

1) What are the three states of matter?

2) Describe how particles are arranged in a liquid.

3) True or false? The colder a gas, the higher the average energy in the kinetic energy stores of its particles.

Density of Materials (p.65-66) ☑

4) True or false? A 100 g cube of gold has the same density as a 200 g cube of gold.

5) Name a unit of density.

6) True or false? Solids are usually denser than gases.

7) Describe how you could find the volume of a cuboid.

8) Briefly describe an experiment to find the density of a liquid.

Internal Energy and Changes of State (p.67-68) ☑

9) What is internal energy?

10) What happens to the particles in a substance when that substance is heated?

11) Name the six changes of state.

12) Is a change of state a physical change or a chemical change?

13) True or false? Mass stays the same when a substance changes state.

14) Explain the cause of the flat sections on a graph of temperature against time for a substance being heated.

15) Sketch a graph of temperature against time for a gas being cooled. Your graph should show the point that the gas turns into a liquid and the point that the liquid turns into a solid.

16) What is specific latent heat?

17) What is meant by specific latent heat of fusion?

Developing the Model of the Atom

You might have thought <u>atomic structure</u> was all Chemistry. But you need to know it for Physics too.

Models of the Atom Have Changed Over Time

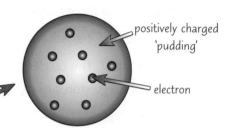

positively charged
'pudding'

electron

1) <u>Scientific models</u> (p.3) change over <u>time</u>. This happens when <u>new evidence</u> is found that <u>can't</u> be explained by the <u>current model</u>.

2) This is what happened with the <u>model of the atom</u>.

3) Scientists used to think that atoms were <u>solid spheres</u>.

4) They then found atoms contain even smaller, negatively charged particles — <u>electrons</u>.

5) This led to a model called the '<u>plum pudding model</u>' being created.

6) The plum pudding model showed the atom as a <u>ball</u> of <u>positive charge</u> with <u>electrons scattered</u> in this ball.

Experiments Showed that the Plum Pudding Model Was Wrong

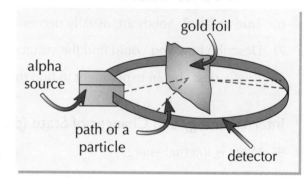

gold foil

alpha source

path of a particle

detector

1) Later, scientists carried out <u>alpha particle scattering experiments</u>. They fired positively charged <u>alpha particles</u> at a very thin sheet of gold.

2) From the plum pudding model, they <u>expected</u> most of the particles to <u>go straight through</u> the sheet. They predicted that a few particles would <u>change direction</u> by a <u>small</u> amount.

3) But instead, some particles changed direction <u>more than expected</u>. A small number even went <u>backwards</u>.

4) This meant the plum pudding model <u>couldn't</u> be right.

5) So, scientists came up with the <u>nuclear model</u> of the atom:

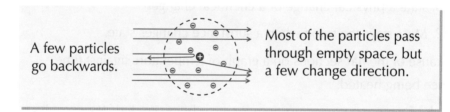

A few particles go backwards.

Most of the particles pass through empty space, but a few change direction.

Nuclear Model of Atom
- There's a tiny, positively charged <u>nucleus</u> at the centre of the atom.
- Most of the <u>mass</u> is in the nucleus.
- The nucleus is surrounded by a 'cloud' of negative <u>electrons</u>.
- Most of the atom is <u>empty space</u>.

Bohr Improved the Nuclear Model

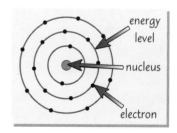

energy level

nucleus

electron

1) <u>Niels Bohr</u> changed the nuclear model of the atom.

2) He suggested that the electrons <u>orbit</u> (go around) the nucleus in <u>energy levels</u>:

3) Each energy level (or shell) is a <u>fixed distance</u> from the nucleus.

4) Bohr's theory was supported by many <u>experiments</u>. Experiments later showed that Bohr's theory was correct.

Developing the Model of the Atom

Bohr's model was pretty good. But the discovery of <u>protons</u> and <u>neutrons</u> made it even better.

The **Nucleus** was Found to Contain **Protons** and **Neutrons**

1) Eventually experiments by scientists showed that the nucleus can be <u>divided</u> into smaller particles. Each particle has the <u>same positive charge</u>. These particles were named <u>protons</u>.

2) Experiments by <u>James Chadwick</u> showed that the nucleus also contained <u>neutral particles</u> — <u>neutrons</u>. This happened about 20 years after scientists agreed that atoms have nuclei.

3) This led to a model of the atom which was <u>pretty close</u> to the one we have today.

You Need to Know the **Current Model** of the Atom

The current model of the atom is a <u>nuclear model</u>.
This means there is a <u>nucleus</u> in the <u>centre</u> surrounded by electrons.

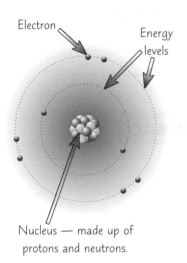

Electron

Energy levels

Nucleus — made up of protons and neutrons.

1) Atoms are <u>very small</u>. The <u>radius</u> of an atom is about 1×10^{-10} m (see p.12 for more on standard form).

2) The <u>nucleus</u> is <u>tiny</u>, but it makes up most of the <u>mass</u> of the atom.

3) The radius of the nucleus is about <u>10 000</u> times smaller than the <u>radius</u> of the <u>atom</u>.

4) The <u>nucleus</u> is made up of <u>protons</u> and <u>neutrons</u>.

5) <u>Protons</u> are <u>positively charged</u> and <u>neutrons</u> have <u>no charge</u>. So the <u>nucleus</u> is <u>positively charged</u>.

6) Electrons have a <u>negative charge</u>. They move <u>around</u> (orbit) the nucleus at different distances.

7) These distances are known as <u>energy levels</u>.

8) <u>Atoms</u> have <u>no overall charge</u>. The <u>number of protons = the number of electrons</u>.

Electrons can **Move** Between **Energy Levels**

1) The <u>further</u> an <u>energy level</u> is from the <u>nucleus</u>, the <u>more energy</u> an electron in that energy level has.

2) <u>Electrons</u> can <u>move between energy levels</u> by <u>absorbing</u> (taking in) or <u>releasing electromagnetic radiation</u> (p.117).

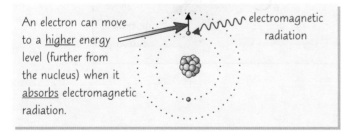

An electron can move to a <u>higher</u> energy level (further from the nucleus) when it <u>absorbs</u> electromagnetic radiation.

electromagnetic radiation

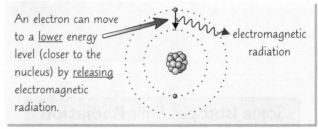

An electron can move to a <u>lower</u> energy level (closer to the nucleus) by <u>releasing</u> electromagnetic radiation.

electromagnetic radiation

3) If an electron in an <u>outer</u> energy level <u>absorbs</u> electromagnetic radiation, it can <u>leave the atom</u>.

4) If an atom <u>loses one or more electrons</u> it turns into a <u>positively charged ion</u>.

WORKING SCIENTIFICALLY

The model of the atom has developed over time...

Due to lots of scientists doing lots of <u>experiments</u>, we now have a better idea of what the atom's really like. We now know about the particles in atoms — <u>protons</u>, <u>neutrons</u> and <u>electrons</u>.

Isotopes

Isotopes of an element look pretty similar, but watch out — they have <u>different numbers of neutrons</u>.

Atoms of the Same Element have the Same Number of Protons

1) The <u>number of protons</u> in an atom is called its <u>atomic number</u>.

2) The <u>protons</u> in a <u>nucleus</u> give the nucleus its <u>positive charge</u>.
So the <u>atomic number</u> of an atom tells you the <u>charge</u> on the <u>nucleus</u>.

3) The <u>mass number</u> of an atom is the <u>sum</u> of the <u>number of protons</u> and the <u>number of neutrons</u>.

4) An <u>element</u> is a substance only containing atoms with the <u>same number of protons</u>.

5) You can <u>show</u> information about an <u>atom</u> of an element like this:

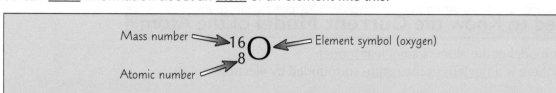

Mass number → 16O ← Element symbol (oxygen)
Atomic number → 8

- Oxygen has an <u>atomic number</u> of 8, this means all oxygen atoms have <u>8 protons</u>.
- This atom of oxygen has a <u>mass number</u> of 16.
Since it has 8 protons, it must have $16 - 8 = $ <u>8 neutrons</u>.

Isotopes are Different Forms of the Same Element

1) <u>Atoms</u> of an element with the <u>same</u> number of <u>protons</u> but a <u>different</u> number of <u>neutrons</u> are called <u>isotopes</u>.

2) Isotopes of an element have the <u>same atomic number</u>, but a <u>different mass number</u>.

Example: <u>Carbon-12</u> and <u>carbon-13</u> are isotopes.

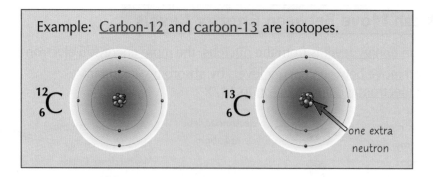

$^{12}_{6}$C $^{13}_{6}$C
one extra neutron

Some Isotopes Emit Radiation

1) Some isotopes are <u>unstable</u>.

2) They <u>emit (give out) radiation</u> from their <u>nuclei</u> to try and become <u>more stable</u>.

3) This process is called <u>radioactive decay</u>.

4) The radiation emitted is called <u>nuclear radiation</u>.

5) There are <u>four different types</u> of nuclear radiation — see the next page.

6) Isotopes that give out nuclear radiation are called <u>radioactive isotopes</u>.

Types of Nuclear Radiation

The four types of nuclear radiation all come from the nucleus, but they have some key differences...

There are Four Types of Nuclear Radiation

Alpha Particles, (α)

An alpha particle is two neutrons and two protons (like a helium nucleus).

Beta Particles, (β)

A beta particle is a fast-moving electron.

Gamma Rays, (γ)

Gamma rays are waves of electromagnetic radiation (p.117).

Neutrons, (n)

Isotopes can also give out neutrons when they decay.

You Need to Know the Properties of Ionising Nuclear Radiation

1) Ionising radiation is radiation that can knock electrons off atoms and turn them into ions.

2) The ionising power of radiation is how easily it can do this.

3) Alpha particles, beta particles and gamma rays are all types of ionising radiation.

4) They all have different properties:

Example: an alpha particle colliding with an atom and ionising it.

emitted electron

atom

Type of radiation	Ionising power	Range in air	Stopped by
alpha particles	strong	a few centimetres	a sheet of paper
beta particles	moderate	a few metres	a sheet of aluminium
gamma rays	weak	a long distance	thick sheets of lead or metres of concrete

'Range in air' is the distance the radiation can travel through air.

5) Their different ionising powers, ranges and abilities to penetrate (get through) materials make them suitable for different uses.

> E.g. A medical tracer is a radioactive isotope that is injected into a patient. The radiation it emits needs to be detected outside the patient's body.
>
> You couldn't use a source of alpha radiation as a medical tracer. Alpha particles wouldn't be able to pass through the body and be detected outside the body. They are also very ionising and so could do a lot of damage (see p.80).
>
> Medical tracers usually emit gamma rays. Gamma rays are only weakly ionising and easily pass through the body. This means they can be easily detected and do less harm than alpha particles.

Alpha particles are more ionising than beta particles...

...and beta particles are more ionising than gamma rays. Make sure you've got that clearly memorised, as well as what makes up each type of radiation, as this isn't the last you'll see of this stuff. No siree.

Nuclear Equations

Nuclear equations show radioactive decay. The next few pages will help you get the hang of them.

Mass and Atomic Numbers Have to Balance

1) Nuclear equations are a way of showing radioactive decay (p.74).

2) They're normally written like this:

> nucleus before decay → nucleus after decay + radiation emitted

3) There is one golden rule to remember:

> The total mass and atomic numbers must be equal on both sides of the arrow.

Alpha Decay Decreases the Charge and Mass of the Nucleus

1) Alpha decay is when an alpha particle is emitted from a radioactive nucleus.

2) An alpha particle is made up of two protons and two neutrons. It is the same as a helium nucleus.

3) When a nucleus emits an alpha particle, its atomic number goes down by 2 and its mass number goes down by 4.

Gamma rays are sometimes also released when a nucleus decays by alpha or beta decay.

4) The charge of the nucleus decreases when it gives out an alpha particle.

5) An alpha particle is usually written as a helium nucleus in a nuclear equation: $^{4}_{2}$He.

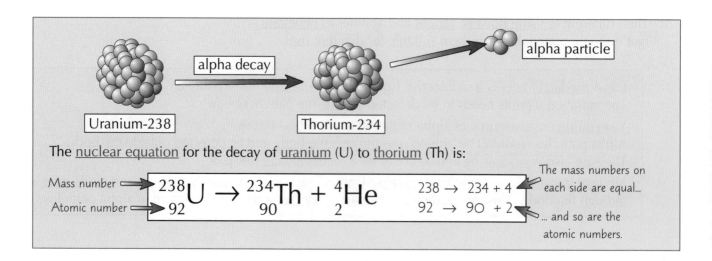

Uranium-238 — alpha decay → Thorium-234 — alpha particle

The nuclear equation for the decay of uranium (U) to thorium (Th) is:

Mass number ⟶
Atomic number ⟶

$$^{238}_{92}U \rightarrow\ ^{234}_{90}Th +\ ^{4}_{2}He$$

$238 \rightarrow 234 + 4$
$92 \rightarrow 90 + 2$

The mass numbers on each side are equal... ... and so are the atomic numbers.

Learn how alpha decay changes the mass and atomic numbers...

In the exam, you might be asked to identify what type of radiation is given out in a decay. If the mass number has dropped by 4 and the atomic number has dropped by 2, it must be alpha.

Nuclear Equations

On the last page you saw how to write <u>nuclear equations</u> for <u>alpha decay</u>. Well, now it's time for <u>beta</u>.

Beta Decay Increases the Charge of the Nucleus

1) <u>Beta decay</u> is when a <u>beta particle</u> is emitted from a <u>radioactive nucleus</u>.

2) During beta decay, a <u>neutron</u> in the nucleus <u>turns into a proton</u>.

3) This means the nucleus has one more <u>proton</u>, so its <u>atomic number</u> goes up by <u>1</u>.

4) It also means the <u>positive charge</u> of the nucleus <u>increases</u>.

5) A <u>beta particle</u> has an <u>atomic number</u> of <u>−1</u> so the atomic numbers balance on each side of the equation.

6) Protons and neutrons have the <u>same mass</u>, so the <u>mass</u> of the nucleus <u>doesn't change</u>.

7) A <u>beta particle</u> is an electron. It is written as $_{-1}^{0}e$ in nuclear equations.

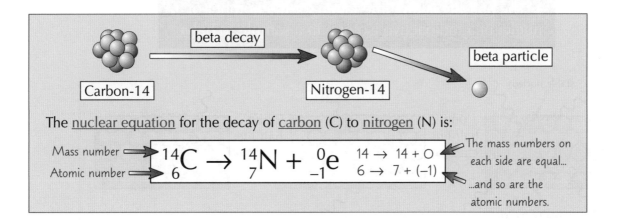

The <u>nuclear equation</u> for the decay of <u>carbon</u> (C) to <u>nitrogen</u> (N) is:

Mass number ⟶
Atomic number ⟶

$$_{6}^{14}C \rightarrow\ _{7}^{14}N +\ _{-1}^{0}e$$

14 → 14 + 0
6 → 7 + (−1)

The mass numbers on each side are equal...
...and so are the atomic numbers.

Gamma Rays Don't Change the Charge or Mass of the Nucleus

1) Gamma rays are a way of getting rid of <u>extra energy</u> from a nucleus.

2) When they are emitted, they don't change the <u>mass</u> or <u>charge</u> of the atom and nucleus.

REVISION TIP

Beta particles are electrons but they come from the nucleus...

It seems a bit odd that beta decay causes the atomic number to <u>increase</u>. It makes sense if you understand what's happening to the particles — beta decay happens when a <u>neutron</u> turns into a <u>proton</u> and an <u>electron</u>. So there's one more proton, and the atomic number = <u>number of protons</u>.

Half-Life

How quickly <u>unstable nuclei</u> decay is measured using <u>activity</u> and <u>half-life</u> — two very important terms.

The **Activity** of a Source is the **Number of Decays per Second**

1) The <u>radiation</u> given out by a <u>radioactive decay</u> can be measured with a <u>Geiger-Muller</u> tube and <u>counter</u> detector.

2) The <u>number of decays</u> the counter measures <u>every second</u> is called the <u>count-rate</u>.

3) The <u>activity</u> of a radioactive source is the <u>rate</u> at which it decays. This means how many <u>unstable nuclei</u> decay <u>every second</u>.

4) Activity is measured in <u>becquerels</u>, <u>Bq</u>. 1 Bq is <u>1 decay per second</u>.

Radioactivity is a Totally **Random Process**

1) Radioactive decay is entirely <u>random</u>. So you <u>can't predict</u> exactly <u>which</u> nucleus in a sample will decay <u>next</u>, or <u>when</u> any one of them will decay.

2) But you <u>can</u> predict <u>how long</u> it will take for half of the <u>nuclei</u> to decay. This is known as a <u>half-life</u>.

> The <u>half-life</u> is the time taken for the <u>number of nuclei</u> of a radioactive isotope in a sample to <u>halve</u>.

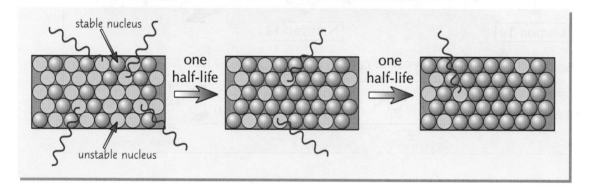

3) Half-life is also the <u>time</u> taken for the <u>count-rate</u> or <u>activity</u> of a sample to fall to <u>half</u> of its <u>initial (starting) value</u>.

4) The half-life of a radioactive sample will <u>always be the same</u>. This means it doesn't matter what activity you <u>start</u> with when doing half-life calculations (see the next page).

Different substances have different half-lives...

Some substances take a <u>long time</u> to <u>decay</u>, giving them a <u>long half-life</u>, while others decay in the blink of an eye. For example, neodymium-144 has a half-life of 2 million billion years, while helium-5 has a half-life of 7.6×10^{-22} seconds. That's 0.00000000000000000000076 seconds. Pretty speedy eh?

Half-Life

You learnt all about what <u>half-life</u> is on the last page, but now it's time to find out how to <u>calculate</u> it.

You Need to be able to **Calculate** a **Half-Life**

1) You may be asked to calculate the <u>half-life</u> of a source.
2) You just need to find out <u>how long</u> it takes for the <u>activity</u> or <u>count-rate</u> of the source to <u>halve</u>.

EXAMPLE: **The activity of a radioactive isotope was measured. Initially it was 64 Bq. 12 seconds later it had fallen to 16 Bq. Calculate the half-life of the sample.**

1) First, find how many half-lives it takes for the activity to fall to from <u>64 Bq</u> to <u>16 Bq</u>.

2) So you know 12 s is equal to <u>two</u> half-lives. <u>Divide 12</u> by <u>2</u> to find <u>one half-life</u>.

After one half life, the activity will be 64 ÷ 2 = 32 Bq
After two half lives, the activity will be 32 ÷ 2 = 16 Bq

*Time for one half life = 12 ÷ 2 = **6 s***

You Can Find the **Half-Life** of a Sample from a **Graph** of its **Activity**

1) A graph of <u>activity against time</u> is <u>always</u> shaped like the one below.

2) The <u>half-life</u> is found from the graph by finding the <u>time interval</u> on the <u>bottom axis</u> corresponding to a <u>halving</u> of the <u>activity</u> on the <u>vertical axis</u>. Easy.

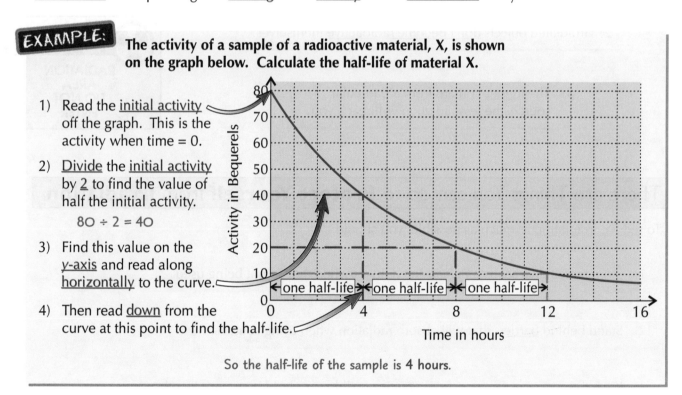

EXAMPLE: **The activity of a sample of a radioactive material, X, is shown on the graph below. Calculate the half-life of material X.**

1) Read the <u>initial activity</u> off the graph. This is the activity when time = 0.

2) <u>Divide</u> the <u>initial activity</u> by <u>2</u> to find the value of half the initial activity.
   80 ÷ 2 = 40

3) Find this value on the <u>y-axis</u> and read along <u>horizontally</u> to the curve.

4) Then read <u>down</u> from the curve at this point to find the half-life.

So the half-life of the sample is 4 hours.

You can get useful information from activity-time graphs...

Make sure you can use <u>graphs</u> like the one above to work out <u>half-lives</u>. All you've got to do is read off the initial <u>activity</u> from the y-axis, then work out what half this activity would be by <u>dividing by two</u>. Then, just read off the time from the x-axis for this value, which is one half-life.

Irradiation and Contamination

You need to be very careful when working with radiation. You don't even need to touch a source to be irradiated by it — just being near it is enough. Make sure you know how to protect yourself.

Ionising Radiation can Damage Cells

1) There are hazards (dangers) you need to protect yourself from when working with radioactive sources.

2) Ionising radiation can enter living cells and ionise (p.75) atoms in them.

3) This can damage the cells. This may cause cancer or kill cells off completely.

> We need to know how radiation affects the human body, so we can protect ourselves from harm.
> So it's really important for research into the effects of radiation to be published and checked by peer review — see page 2.

Exposure to Radiation is called Irradiation

1) Objects near a radioactive source can be irradiated by it. This means radiation from the radioactive source will reach the object.

2) Irradiated objects don't become radioactive themselves.

3) The further you are from a particular source, the less radiation will reach you.

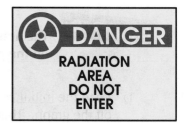

There are Things You can do to Protect Yourself from Irradiation

To reduce irradiation as much as possible, you should:

1) Store radioactive sources in lead-lined boxes when they're not being used.

2) Stand behind barriers that will absorb radiation when using sources.

3) Keep the source as far away from you as possible, e.g. hold it at arm's length.

Safety precautions can help protect against hazards from radiation...

Radiation can be pretty dangerous stuff, so it's important to protect yourself when you're working with radioactive substances. Lead is often used to line storage boxes and in protective screens because it is very good at absorbing radiation, so it stops a lot of the radiation from reaching what's on the other side.

Irradiation and Contamination

On the previous page you saw how irradiation can result from even just being near a source.
Now for radioactive contamination. This only happens if you touch or breathe in a radioactive substance.

Contamination is Radioactive Particles Getting Onto Objects

1) If unwanted radioactive atoms get onto or into an object,
the object is contaminated.

2) These contaminating atoms might then decay and release
radiation which could harm you.

3) Being contaminated by a source may cause more damage than if you
are irradiated by the same source, as you may carry it for a long time.

4) To help stop contamination, you should wear gloves
and use tongs when handling radioactive sources.

People whose jobs involve
radioactive materials often wear
protective suits and face masks to
help stop them being contaminated.

Irradiation and Contamination Dangers Depend on the Source

The amount of harm contamination or irradiation by a source can cause depends on the radiation type.

Irradiation

1) Beta and gamma sources are the most dangerous to be irradiated by. These types of
radiation have long ranges (p.75). That means more radiation will reach you from a
beta or gamma source than from an alpha source at the same distance.

2) They can also penetrate (travel through) your body and may damage your
organs. Alpha is less dangerous because it can't get through the skin
and is easily blocked, e.g. by a small air gap (p.75).

Contamination

1) INSIDE the body, alpha sources are the most dangerous to be contaminated by.
This is because alpha particles are the most ionising type of radiation.

2) Beta particles and gamma rays are less damaging because they are less ionising.

3) Gamma sources are the least dangerous inside the body.
This is because gamma rays are the least ionising type of radiation
and they mostly pass straight out without doing any damage.

4) OUTSIDE of the body, an alpha source is
the least dangerous to be contaminated by.
This is because alpha particles can't get
through the skin and damage your organs.

Warm-Up & Exam Questions

Atoms may be tiny, but you could bag some big marks in your exams if you know them inside-out. Here are some questions to check just how great your understanding of atoms and radiation really is...

Warm-Up Questions

1) Why was the plum pudding model of an atom replaced with a nuclear model?
2) Describe our current nuclear model of the atom.
3) What is emitted when an electron moves to a lower energy level?
4) What does an atom become if it loses an electron?
5) What does the mass number tell you about an atom?
6) Describe what happens to the mass number and atomic number of an atom if it undergoes alpha decay. What happens to them if the atom undergoes gamma decay?
7) What is the difference between contamination and irradiation by a radioactive source?
8) Why are gamma sources the least dangerous type of radioactive source to have inside you?

Exam Questions

1 Two different atoms can be isotopes of one another.

Grade 1-3

1.1 Name the particles found in the nucleus of an atom.

[2 marks]

1.2 What is meant by the term **isotopes**?

☐ Atoms with the same atomic number but a different mass number

☐ Atoms with the same mass number but a different atomic number

☐ Atoms with the same number of protons but a different atomic number

☐ Atoms with the same number of neutrons but a different number of electrons

[1 mark]

2 **Table 1** shows some information about iodine-131 ($^{131}_{53}$I), an isotope of iodine.

Grade 3-4

Table 1

Particle	Type of Charge	Number present in an atom of iodine-131
Proton	positive	
Neutron	zero	
Electron		53

Complete **Table 1**.

[3 marks]

Topic 4 — Atomic Structure

Exam Questions

3 This question is about the effects on the nucleus of different types of radioactive decay. [Grade 4-5]
Draw **one** line from each description to the correct type of decay.

| Both the mass and charge of the nucleus change. | | alpha |

| Neither the mass or charge of the nucleus changes. | | beta |

| | | gamma |

| The charge of the nucleus changes but the mass stays the same. | | neutron |

[3 marks]

4 Sources A, B and C each emit a single type of radiation. Radiation from each source [Grade 4-5]
was directed at thin sheets of paper and aluminium. A detector was used to measure
where radiation had passed through the sheets. The results are shown in **Figure 1**.

Figure 1

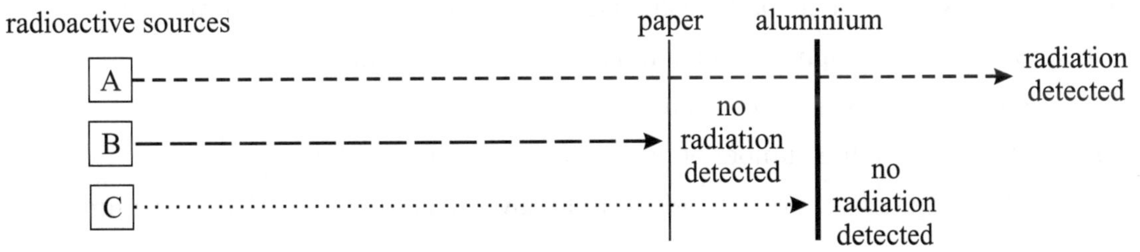

4.1 Name the type of radiation that source C emits. Explain your answer.

[2 marks]

4.2 Give **one** example of a detector that could have been used to detect the radiation.

[1 mark]

5 A student measured the activity of a radioactive source every 10 minutes. [Grade 4-5]
Her results are shown in **Table 2**.

Table 2

Time (mins)	0	10	20	30	40	50
Activity (Bq)	740	575	450	350	270	210

5.1 Which value below is the half-life of the source?

☐ 20 minutes ☐ 28 minutes ☐ 34 minutes ☐ 40 minutes

[1 mark]

5.2 The source emits only alpha radiation. It must be removed from a lead-lined box before the
activity can be measured. The student believes that they should be more concerned about
avoiding contamination by the source rather than irradiation by it. Suggest why.

[2 marks]

Revision Summary for Topic 4

Well, that's the end of Topic 4 — hopefully it wasn't too painful. Time to see how much you've absorbed.
- Try these questions and tick off each one when you get it right.
- When you've done all the questions under a heading, and are completely happy with it, tick it off.

The Atomic Model and Isotopes (p.72-74) ☑

1) What is the overall charge of an atom? ☑

2) How much bigger is the radius of the atom than the radius of the nucleus? ☑
   a) 10 times bigger   b) 1000 times bigger   c) 10 000 times bigger

3) What happens when an electron in an atom absorbs electromagnetic radiation? ☑

4) What happens to an atom if it loses one or more of its electrons? ☑

Nuclear Decay and Half-life (p.75-79) ☑

5) What is the atomic number of an atom? ☑

6) Which number is the same for all atoms of an element: the atomic number or the mass number? ☑

7) How do atoms of two isotopes of an element differ from each other? ☑

8) For the three types of ionising nuclear radiation, give:
   a) their ionising power, b) their range in air. ☑

9) How does the emission of a beta particle change the atomic number of an atom? ☑

10) Draw the symbols used for alpha and beta radiation in nuclear equations. ☑

11) What is the activity of a substance measured in? ☑

12) Define half-life in terms of the number of nuclei of a radioactive isotope. ☑

13) Describe how to find a radioactive source's half-life, given a graph of its activity over time. ☑

Irradiation and Contamination (p.80-81) ☑

14) Why is it important that findings from research into the effects of radiation on
    humans is published in scientific journals? ☑

15) What is irradiation? ☑

16) Give two examples of how to stop: a) contamination,   b) irradiation. ☑

17) Compare the hazards of being irradiated and contaminated by a gamma source. ☑

Contact and Non-Contact Forces

When you're talking about the <u>forces</u> acting on an object, it's not enough to just talk about the <u>size</u> of each force. You need to know their <u>direction</u> too — force is a <u>vector</u>, with a size and a direction.

Force is a **Vector** Quantity

1) Vector quantities have a <u>magnitude (size)</u> and a <u>direction</u>. For example:

> <u>Vector quantities</u>: force, velocity, displacement, acceleration, momentum

2) Some quantities have a magnitude but <u>no direction</u>. These are called <u>scalar quantities</u>. Here are some examples of scalar quantities:

> <u>Scalar quantities</u>: speed, distance, mass, temperature, time

3) Vectors are usually represented by an <u>arrow</u>.
4) The <u>length</u> of the arrow shows the <u>magnitude</u>.
5) The <u>direction</u> of the arrow shows the <u>direction of the quantity</u>.

Forces Can be **Contact** or **Non-Contact**

1) A <u>force</u> is a <u>push</u> or a <u>pull</u> that acts on an object.
2) Forces are caused by objects <u>interacting</u> with each other.
3) All forces are either <u>contact</u> or <u>non-contact</u> forces.
4) When <u>two objects</u> have to be <u>touching</u> for a force to act, the force is a <u>contact force</u>.

> <u>Contact force examples</u>: friction, air resistance, tension, normal contact force

When an object exerts a force on a second object, the second object pushes back. This is the normal contact force.

5) If the objects <u>do not need to be touching</u> for the force to act, the force is a <u>non-contact force</u>.

> <u>Non-contact force examples</u>: magnetic force, gravitational force, electrostatic force

6) When two objects <u>interact</u>, a <u>force</u> is produced on <u>both</u> objects. The forces on the two objects are <u>equal in size</u> but act in <u>opposite directions</u>.
7) These two forces are called an <u>interaction pair</u>.

- The <u>gravitational attraction</u> between the Earth and the Sun is an example of an <u>interaction pair</u>.
- A gravitational force acts on the Earth <u>attracting</u> it to the Sun.
- At the same time a force acts on the Sun <u>attracting</u> it towards the Earth.
- These forces are the <u>same size</u> but act in <u>opposite directions</u>.

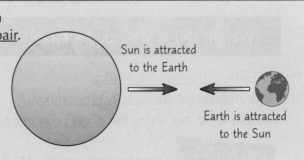

Sun is attracted to the Earth

Earth is attracted to the Sun

An interaction between two objects produces a force on each object...

Whether it's a <u>contact</u> or <u>non-contact</u> force, it's always acting as part of a <u>pair</u>. Remember it's the two <u>forces</u>, not the objects, which are called the <u>interaction pair</u> — and they are <u>always equal and opposite</u>.

Weight, Mass and Gravity

Mass and weight are <u>NOT</u> the same... Read on to find out <u>why</u>. You know you want to.

Mass is Measured in kg

1) <u>Mass</u> is just the amount of <u>matter (stuff)</u> in an object.

2) It's measured in <u>kilograms</u>, kg.

3) Scientists sometimes think of all the mass in an object as being at <u>one single point</u> in the object.

4) This point is called the <u>centre of mass</u>.

Weight is Measured in Newtons

1) <u>Weight</u> is the <u>force</u> acting on an object due to <u>gravity</u>.

2) You can think of this force as acting from an object's <u>centre of mass</u>.

3) Close to Earth, this force is caused by the <u>gravitational field</u> around the Earth.

4) The <u>weight</u> of an object depends on its <u>mass</u> and the <u>strength of the gravitational field</u> it's in.

5) The <u>gravitational field strength of Earth</u> changes slightly depending on <u>where you are</u>.

6) So the weight of an object depends on its <u>location</u>.

7) Unlike the <u>mass</u> of an object which is <u>always the same</u>.

8) Weight is measured in <u>newtons</u>, <u>N</u>.

9) It can be measured with a calibrated <u>spring</u> balance (or <u>newtonmeter</u>).

centre of mass

weight

Mass and Weight are Directly Proportional

1) You can calculate the <u>weight</u> of an object if you know its <u>mass</u> (*m*) and the <u>strength</u> of the <u>gravitational field</u> that it is in (*g*):

Weight (N) = Mass (kg) × Gravitational Field Strength (N/kg)

2) For Earth, <u>g is around 9.8 N/kg</u>.

3) Mass and weight are <u>directly proportional</u>.

4) You can write this, using the <u>direct proportionality symbol</u>, as $W \propto m$.

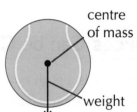

EXAMPLE: **A motorcycle weighs 2450 N on Earth.**
Calculate the mass of the motorcycle. (g = 9.8 N/kg)

1) First, <u>rearrange</u> $W = mg$ to find <u>mass</u>.   mass = weight ÷ gravitational field strength
2) Then, put in the numbers   mass = 2450 ÷ 9.8 = **250 kg**
   to <u>calculate</u> the mass.

Resultant Forces and Work Done

I'm sure you're no stranger to <u>doing work</u>, but in physics it's all to do with <u>transferring energy</u>.

A **Resultant Force** is the **Overall Force** on a Point or Object

1) If a <u>number of forces</u> act at a single point, you can replace them with a <u>single force</u>.
2) This single force is called the <u>resultant force</u>.
3) It has the <u>same effect</u> as all the original forces added together.
4) You can find the resultant force when forces are acting in a <u>straight line</u>.
   <u>Add together</u> forces acting in the <u>same</u> direction and <u>take away</u> any going in the <u>opposite</u> direction.

> A <u>trolley</u> is pulled by two children. One child pulls the trolley with a force of 5 N to the <u>left</u>. The other pulls the trolley with a force of 10 N to the <u>right</u>.
>
> 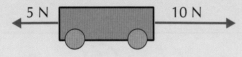 5 N   10 N
>
> So the resultant force, F, is:
> $F = 10\text{ N} - 5\text{ N}$
> $= \underline{5\text{ N to the right}}$.

If a Force **Moves** an Object, **Work is Done**

> When a <u>force</u> moves an object through a <u>distance</u>,
> <u>energy is transferred</u> and <u>work is done</u> on the object.

1) To make an object move, a force <u>must</u> act on it.
2) The force does '<u>work</u>' to move the object.
3) This causes <u>energy</u> to be <u>transferred to</u> the object.
4) The force usually <u>does work</u> against frictional forces too.
5) Doing work against frictional forces causes energy to be transferred to the <u>thermal energy store</u> of the object.
6) This causes the <u>temperature</u> of the object to <u>increase</u>.

'Work done' and 'energy transferred' are the same thing. You need to be able to <u>describe</u> how energy is transferred when work is done. Look back at p.20 for more on this.

- When you <u>push</u> something along a <u>rough surface</u> (like a <u>carpet</u>) you are doing work <u>against frictional forces</u>.
- Some energy is <u>transferred</u> to the <u>kinetic energy store</u> of the <u>object</u> because it starts <u>moving</u>.
- Some is also transferred to <u>thermal energy stores</u> due to the work done against friction.
- This causes the overall <u>temperature</u> of the object to <u>increase</u>.

7) You can find out <u>how much work</u> has been done using:

The line of action of the force is the direction of the force.

Work done (J) ——— $W = Fs$ ——— Force (N)

Distance (moved along the line of action of the force) (m)

8) <u>One joule of work</u> is done when a <u>force of one newton</u> causes an object to move a <u>distance of one metre</u> in the direction of the force.
9) You need to be able to <u>convert</u> joules to newton metres: <u>1 J = 1 Nm</u>.

Warm-Up & Exam Questions

Now you've learnt the basics of forces, it's time to act on your new knowledge.
Give these questions a go and test how well you've forced those facts into your brain.

Warm-Up Questions

1) Which of the following is a contact force: magnetic force, gravitational force or friction?
2) Vectors can be drawn as arrows. What is represented by the length of the arrow?
3) State the units of: a) mass, b) weight.
4) If two forces are acting in the same direction, how can you find the resultant force?

Exam Questions

1 Most quantities can be divided into two groups: scalars and vectors. *(Grade 1-3)*

1.1 Which of the following is a vector? Tick **one** box.

☐ speed ☐ time ☐ mass ☐ force

[1 mark]

1.2 Which of the following is a scalar? Tick **one** box.

☐ 14 kg ☐ 300 kN down ☐ 24 m/s west ☐ 1 m/s² up

[1 mark]

2 **Figure 1** shows two hot air balloons, labelled with the forces acting on them. *(Grade 3-4)*

Figure 1

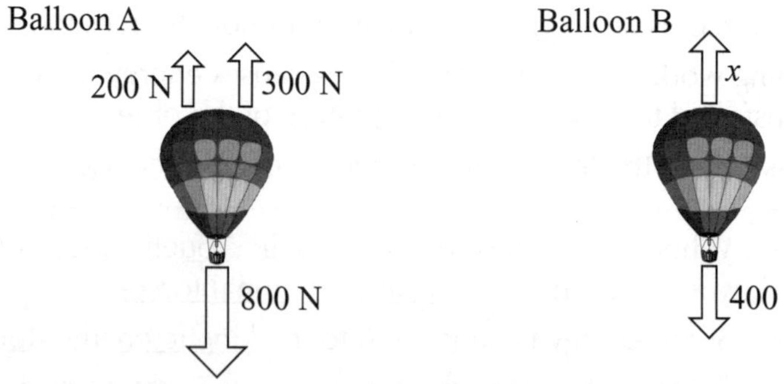

Balloon A

200 N ⇧ ⇧ 300 N

800 N

Balloon B

⇧ x

400 N

2.1 Calculate the size of the resultant force acting on Balloon A and give its direction.

[2 marks]

2.2 The resultant force acting on Balloon B is zero. Calculate the size of force *x*.

[1 mark]

3 A train moves 750 m in a straight line along a flat track.
The resultant force acting on the train is 44 000 N forwards along the track. *(Grade 4-5)*

3.1 Write down the equation that links work done, force and distance.

[1 mark]

3.2 Calculate the work done by the resultant force as the train moves. Give your answer in kilojoules.

[3 marks]

Forces and Elasticity

Forces don't just make objects <u>move</u>, they can also make them <u>deform</u> (change shape).

Stretching, Compressing or Bending Transfers Energy

1) When you apply a force to an object you may cause it to <u>deform</u> (<u>stretch</u>, <u>compress</u> or <u>bend</u>).

2) To do this, you need <u>more than one</u> force acting on the object. <u>One</u> force would just make the object <u>move</u>, not change its shape.

3) An object has been <u>elastically deformed</u> if it can <u>go back</u> to its <u>original shape</u> and <u>length</u> after the force has been removed.

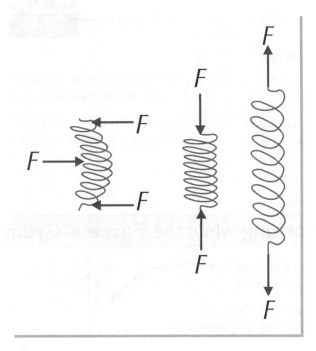

4) If the object <u>doesn't</u> go back to how it was, it has been <u>inelastically deformed</u>.

5) Objects that can be elastically deformed are called <u>elastic objects</u> (e.g. a spring).

6) <u>Work is done</u> when a force stretches or compresses an object. This causes energy to be transferred to the <u>elastic potential energy</u> store of the object.

Elastic objects are only elastic up to a certain point...

Remember the difference between <u>elastic deformation</u> and <u>inelastic deformation</u>. If an <u>object</u> has been <u>elastically deformed</u>, it will <u>return</u> to its <u>original shape</u> when you <u>remove the force</u>. If it's been <u>inelastically deformed</u>, its shape will have been <u>changed permanently</u> — for example, an over-stretched spring will stay stretched even after you remove the force.

Forces and Elasticity

Springs obey a really handy little equation that relates the force on them to their extension — for a while at least. Thankfully, you can plot a graph to see where this equation is true.

Extension is Directly Proportional to Force...

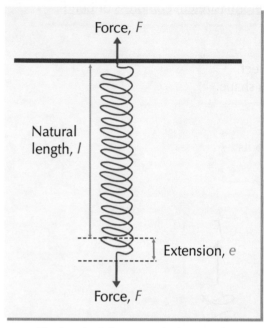

Force, F

Natural
length, l

Extension, e

Force, F

The length of the unstretched spring is sometimes called the spring's natural length.

1) When a force stretches a spring, it causes it to extend.

2) This extension is the difference in length between the stretched and unstretched spring.

3) Up to a given force, the extension is directly proportional to force.

4) So long as a spring hasn't been stretched past its limit of proportionality (see below), you can use:

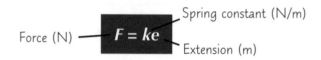

Spring constant (N/m)

Force (N) —— $F = ke$

Extension (m)

5) The spring constant depends on the object that you are stretching.

6) The equation also works for compression (where e is the difference between the natural and compressed lengths).

...but this Stops Working when the Force is Great Enough

1) You can plot a graph of the force applied to a spring and the extension caused.

2) When the graph is a straight line, there is a linear relationship between force and extension.

3) This shows force and extension are directly proportional.

4) The gradient of the straight line is equal to k, the spring constant.

5) When the line begins to bend, the relationship is now non-linear. Force and extension are no longer directly proportional.

6) Point P on the graph (when the line starts to bend) is the limit of proportionality. Past this point, the equation $F = ke$ is no longer true.

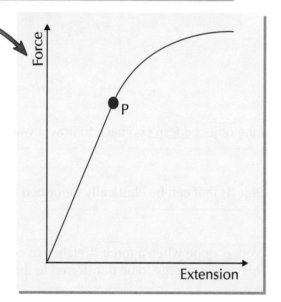

Force

P

Extension

EXAM TIP

The spring constant is measured in N/m...

Be careful with units when doing calculations with springs. Your values for extension will usually be in centimetres or millimetres, but the spring constant is measured in newtons per metre. So convert the extension into metres before you do any calculations, or you'll get the wrong answer.

Investigating Springs

Oh look, here's one of those <u>Required Practicals</u>... There might be a few ways this experiment can <u>stretch</u> you. <u>Read on</u> and take your time with <u>each step</u>, so you won't be past your limits in the exam.

You Can **Investigate** the Link Between **Force** and **Extension**

1) Set up the <u>apparatus</u> as shown in the diagram.

2) Measure the <u>mass</u> of each mass.

3) Calculate its <u>weight</u> (the <u>force</u> applied) using $W = mg$ (p.86).

4) Measure the original (natural) <u>length</u> of the spring.

5) Add a mass to the spring and allow it to come to <u>rest</u>.

6) Record the force and measure the new <u>length</u> of the spring.

7) Find the <u>extension</u>.

extension = new length – original length

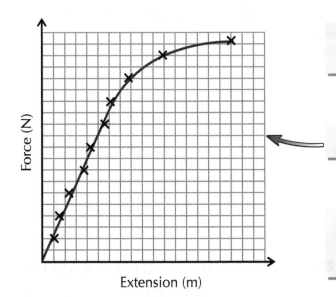

8) <u>Repeat</u> steps 5 to 7 until you've added all the masses.

9) <u>Plot</u> a <u>force-extension graph</u> of your results.

10) You should make sure you have <u>at least</u> 5 measurements before the <u>limit of proportionality</u> (where the line starts to curve).

Investigating Springs

Believe it or not there's another <u>equation</u> involving the <u>extension</u> of a spring — lucky you.

You Can **Work Out Energy Stored** for **Linear** Relationships

1) If a spring is not stretched <u>past</u> its <u>limit of proportionality</u>, the <u>work done</u> in stretching the spring can be found using:

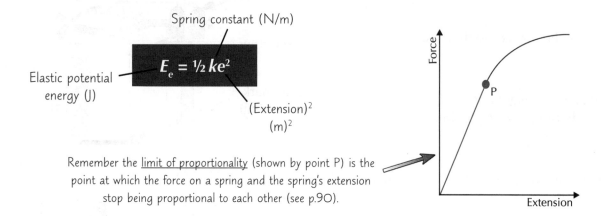

Spring constant (N/m)

Elastic potential energy (J)

$$E_e = \tfrac{1}{2} ke^2$$

(Extension)^2 (m)^2

Remember the <u>limit of proportionality</u> (shown by point P) is the point at which the force on a spring and the spring's extension stop being proportional to each other (see p.90).

2) For an <u>elastic deformation</u>, this formula can be used to calculate the energy stored in a spring's <u>elastic potential energy store</u>.

3) It's also the energy <u>transferred to</u> the spring as it's <u>deformed</u>, or <u>transferred by</u> the spring as it returns to its <u>original shape</u>.

EXAMPLE:

A spring with a spring constant of 50 N/m extends elastically by 10 cm. It doesn't pass its limit of proportionality. Calculate the amount of energy stored in its elastic potential energy store.

You can also use this equation to calculate the energy stored when a spring is compressed.

1) First, you need to <u>convert</u> the extension of the spring into <u>metres</u>.

10 cm ÷ 100 = 0.1 m

2) Then put in the <u>numbers</u> you've been given.

$E_e = \tfrac{1}{2}ke^2 = 0.5 \times 50 \times 0.1^2$
    $= 0.25$ J

Elastic potential energy is equal to the work done to stretch a spring...

As a spring is stretched <u>work is done</u> and the <u>energy is transferred</u> to the spring's <u>elastic potential energy store</u>, so the two are <u>equal</u>. This means the equation for elastic potential energy can be used to calculate work done — but <u>remember</u> it only works before the <u>limit of proportionality</u> is passed.

Warm-Up & Exam Questions

It's time to stretch those thinking muscles with another round of questions. Give these a go to test the limits of your newly extended knowledge of springs and elasticity.

Warm-Up Questions

1) True or false? An object which is inelastically deformed will not return to its original shape when the force is removed.

2) True or false? The formula $F = ke$ cannot be used if a spring is compressed.

3) What units must extension be in before you use the formula for work done on a spring?

Exam Questions

1 A force of 4 N is applied to a spring which causes the spring to extend elastically by 0.05 m.

1.1 Write down the equation which links force, extension and the spring constant.

[1 mark]

1.2 Calculate the spring constant of the spring.

[3 marks]

PRACTICAL

2 A teacher does an experiment to show how a spring extends when masses are hung from it, using the setup shown in **Figure 1**.

He hangs a number of 90 g masses from a 50 g hook attached to the base of the spring. He records the extension of the spring and the total weight of the masses and hook each time he adds a mass to the bottom of the spring.

2.1 State **one** control variable in this experiment.

[1 mark]

2.2 State the independent variable in this experiment.

[1 mark]

Figure 1

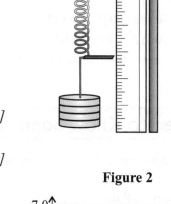

Figure 2 shows the force-extension graph of the results of the experiment.

2.3 Calculate the work done when the spring is stretched with a force of 7.0 N. The spring constant is 175 N/m. Use the correct equation from the Physics Equation Sheet on the inside back cover.

Choose the correct unit from the box.

| N/m | J | cm |

[3 marks]

Figure 2

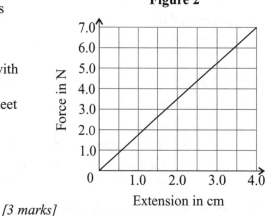

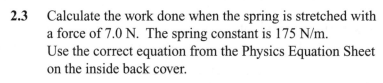

Distance, Displacement, Speed, Velocity

This page is about a bunch of scalars and vectors. Still a little unsure on the difference between scalar and vector quantities? Take a look back at p.85 before starting this page.

Distance is a **Scalar**, Displacement is a **Vector**

1) Distance is just how far an object has moved.
2) Distance is a scalar quantity (p.85), so it doesn't involve direction.
3) Displacement is a vector quantity.
4) It measures the distance and direction in a straight line from an object's starting point to its finishing point.
5) The direction could be in relation to a point, e.g. towards the school.
6) If you walk 5 m north, then 5 m south, your displacement is 0 m but the distance travelled is 10 m.

Speed and **Velocity** are Both **How Fast You're Going**

1) Speed is a scalar and velocity is a vector:

> Speed is just how fast you're going (e.g. 30 mph or 20 m/s) with no regard to the direction.
> Velocity is speed in a given direction, e.g. 30 mph north or 20 m/s to the right.

2) To measure the speed of an object that's moving with a constant speed, time how long it takes the object to travel a certain distance. Make sure you use the correct equipment (see p.134).
3) You can then calculate the object's speed using this formula:

$$s = vt$$ | distance travelled (m) = speed (m/s) × time (s)

4) Objects rarely travel at a constant speed.
5) When you walk, run or travel in a car, your speed is always changing.
6) In these cases, the formula above gives the average (mean) speed during that time.

You Need to Know Some **Typical** Everyday **Speeds**

1) You need to know the typical (usual) speeds of objects:

A person walking — 1.5 m/s	A person cycling — 6 m/s	A train — 30 m/s
A person running — 3 m/s	A car — 25 m/s	A passenger plane — 250 m/s

2) Lots of different things can affect the speed something travels at.
3) The speed at which a person can walk, run or cycle depends on, among other things:

- their fitness
- their age
- the distance they've travelled
- the terrain (what type of ground they are on)

4) The speeds of sound and wind also vary. A typical speed for sound in air is 330 m/s.

Acceleration

Acceleration is the rate of change of velocity — if it stays constant, there's a handy equation you can use.

Acceleration is How **Quickly** You're **Speeding Up**

1) Acceleration is the change in velocity in a certain amount of time.

2) You can find the average acceleration of an object using:

Acceleration (m/s²)
Change in velocity (m/s)
$$a = \frac{\Delta v}{t}$$
Time taken (s)

3) Deceleration (when something slows down) is just negative acceleration.

You Need to be Able to **Estimate Accelerations**

You might have to estimate the acceleration of an object.
To do this, you need the typical speeds from the previous page:

An estimate is just a guess using rough numbers for things.

EXAMPLE: **A man gets onto a bike and accelerates to a typical speed from stationary in 10 seconds. Estimate the acceleration of the bicycle.**

1) First, give a sensible speed for the bicycle to be travelling at.

The typical speed of a bike is about 6 m/s.
The bicycle accelerates in 10 s.

2) Put these numbers into the acceleration equation.

$a = \Delta v \div t$
$= 6 \div 10 = 0.6$ m/s²

3) The ~ symbol just means it's an approximate answer.

So the acceleration is ~0.6 m/s²

Uniform Acceleration Means a **Constant Acceleration**

1) Constant acceleration is sometimes called uniform acceleration.

2) Acceleration due to gravity (g) is uniform for objects falling freely.

3) It's roughly equal to 9.8 m/s² near the Earth's surface.

4) You can use this equation for uniform acceleration:

(Final velocity)²
(m/s)²
Acceleration (m/s²)
$$v^2 - u^2 = 2as$$
Distance (m)
(Initial velocity)² (m/s)²

Initial velocity is just the starting velocity of the object.

EXAMPLE: **A van travelling at 23 m/s starts decelerating uniformly at 2.0 m/s² as it heads towards a built-up area 112 m away. What will its speed be when it reaches the built-up area?**

1) First, rearrange the equation so v^2 is on one side.

$v^2 = u^2 + 2as$

2) Now put the numbers in — remember a is negative because it's a deceleration.

$v^2 = 23^2 + (2 \times -2.0 \times 112)$
$= 81$

3) Finally, square root the whole thing.

$v = \sqrt{81} = $ **9 m/s**

Distance-Time Graphs

You need to be able to <u>draw</u> and <u>understand distance-time graphs</u>.

You Can **Show Journeys** on **Distance-Time Graphs**

1) If an object moves in a <u>straight line</u>, the <u>distance</u> it travels can be plotted on a <u>distance-time</u> graph.

2) You may be asked to <u>draw</u> a distance-time graph for a journey.

3) Or you might have to <u>describe</u> a journey if you're shown a distance-time graph.

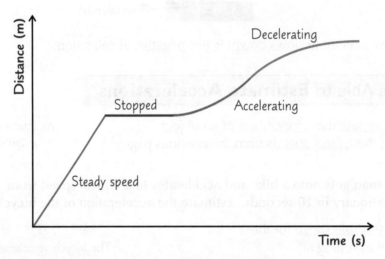

- <u>Gradient = speed</u>. The <u>steeper</u> the graph, the <u>faster</u> it's going.
- <u>Flat</u> sections are where it's <u>stationary</u> — it's <u>stopped</u>.
- <u>Straight</u> uphill (/) sections mean it is travelling at a <u>steady speed</u>.
- <u>Curves</u> represent <u>acceleration</u> or <u>deceleration</u> (p.95).
- A curve that is <u>getting steeper</u> means it's <u>speeding up</u> (accelerating).
- A <u>levelling off</u> curve means it's <u>slowing down</u> (decelerating).

4) You might also have to <u>calculate</u> an object's <u>speed</u> from the graph:

EXAMPLE:

Using the distance-time graph on the right, calculate the speed of the car.

1) The <u>gradient</u> of the graph is the <u>speed</u> of the car.

2) Gradient = $\dfrac{\text{change in vertical axis}}{\text{change in horizontal axis}}$.

3) Draw a <u>large triangle</u>, that takes up most of the straight line.

4) Use the <u>horizontal</u> side of the triangle to find the change in time.

5) Use the <u>vertical side</u> of the triangle to find the change in distance.

6) Put the values for vertical and horizontal into the <u>equation</u>.

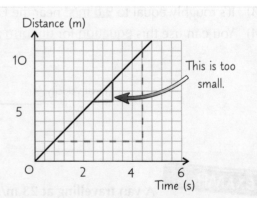

Change in time = 4.4 − 0.8 = 3.6 s

Change in distance = 11 − 2 = 9 m

Gradient = 9 ÷ 3.6 = 2.5

So speed = **2.5 m/s**

Velocity-Time Graphs

You also need to know about <u>velocity-time graphs</u> — they can be used to calculate <u>acceleration</u>.

Journeys Can be Shown on a Velocity-Time Graph

1) How an object's <u>velocity</u> changes as it travels can be plotted on a <u>velocity-time</u> graph.

2) You might have to <u>draw</u> a velocity-time graph for a journey.

3) Or you might have to <u>describe</u> a journey from a velocity-time graph.

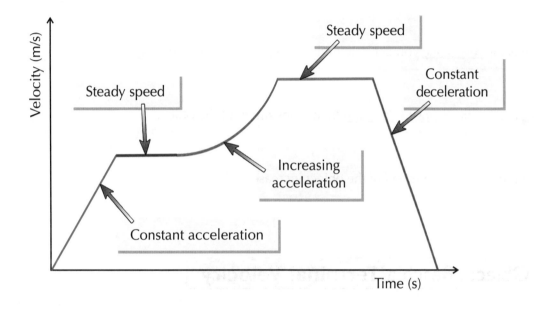

1) <u>Gradient = acceleration</u>. You can calculate this with a similar method to the example on the last page.

2) <u>Flat sections</u> represent travelling at a <u>steady speed</u>.

3) The <u>steeper</u> the graph, the <u>greater</u> the <u>acceleration</u> or <u>deceleration</u>.

4) <u>Uphill</u> sections (/) are <u>acceleration</u>.

5) <u>Downhill</u> sections (\) are <u>deceleration</u>.

6) A <u>curve</u> means <u>changing acceleration</u>.

Read the axes of any graph you get given carefully...

Make sure you don't get <u>confused</u> between <u>distance-time graphs</u> and <u>velocity-time graphs</u>. They can <u>look similar</u>, but <u>different parts</u> of the graphs tell you very different things about the motion of an object.

Drag and Terminal Velocity

If an object <u>falls</u> for long enough, it will reach its <u>terminal velocity</u>. It's all about <u>balance</u> between <u>weight</u> and <u>air resistance</u>. <u>Parachutes</u> work by <u>decreasing</u> your terminal velocity.

Drag Always **Slows Things Down**

1) Gases and liquids are both <u>fluids</u>.

2) Objects moving through fluids experience <u>drag</u>.

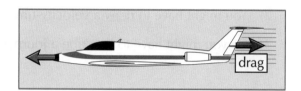

3) Drag is the <u>resistance</u> you get in a fluid. <u>Air resistance</u> is a type of <u>drag</u>.

4) <u>Drag</u> acts in the <u>opposite direction</u> to the movement of the object.

5) Drag <u>increases</u> as the speed of the object increases.

Falling Objects Reach a **Terminal Velocity**

1) When an object first <u>starts falling</u>, the force of gravity is <u>much larger</u> than the drag slowing it down.

2) This means the object <u>accelerates</u> (the object <u>speeds up</u>).

3) As the <u>speed increases</u>, so does the drag.

4) This <u>reduces</u> the <u>acceleration</u> until the drag is <u>equal</u> to the gravitational force. The <u>resultant force</u> (p.87) on the object is then <u>zero</u>.

5) The object will fall at a <u>constant speed</u>. This speed is called its <u>terminal velocity</u>.

All objects falling in air have a terminal velocity...

...but some hit the ground before they reach it. When a falling object is at its <u>terminal velocity</u> the resultant force acting on the object is <u>zero</u>. This doesn't mean the object stops moving, it just means that it <u>stops accelerating</u> — so it continues to fall at a <u>constant speed</u> (its terminal velocity).

Warm-Up & Exam Questions

Slow down, it's not quite time to move on to Newton's Laws just yet. First it's time to check that all the stuff you've just read is still running around your brain. Dive into these questions.

Warm-Up Questions

1) What is the difference between speed and velocity?
2) Suggest the typical speeds of: a) a person running, b) a train, c) a plane.
3) True or false? Acceleration is shown as a curve on a distance-time graph.
4) An object travelling at a steady speed will be represented by which of the following on a velocity-time graph? a) an uphill section, b) a downhill section, c) a flat section.
5) What is the resultant force acting on object falling at its terminal velocity?

Exam Questions

1 A cyclist travels from his house to his local shops.

It takes the cyclist 20 seconds to accelerate from 2.0 m/s to 10 m/s with a steady acceleration. Using the following formula, calculate the cyclist's acceleration:
acceleration = change in velocity ÷ time

[2 marks]

2 **Figure 1** shows the velocity-time graph of a cyclist.

2.1 Describe the motion of the cyclist between 5 and 10 seconds.

[2 marks]

2.2 Calculate the acceleration of the cyclist between 2 and 5 seconds.

[2 marks]

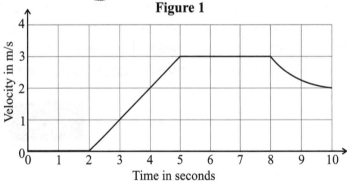

Figure 1

Velocity in m/s vs Time in seconds

3 A coin is rolled in a straight line along a balcony edge at a steady speed of 0.46 m/s.

3.1 Write the equation which links speed, distance and time.

[1 mark]

3.2 Calculate how far the coin rolls in 2.4 s. Give your answer to two significant figures.

[3 marks]

3.3 Another coin is dropped from a height of 8 m.
It accelerates from rest at a constant rate and hits the ground at a speed of 12 m/s.
Calculate the acceleration of the coin during its fall.
Use the correct equation from the Physics Equation Sheet on the inside back cover.

[3 marks]

Newton's First and Second Law

In the 1660s, Isaac Newton worked out some really useful Laws of Motion. Here are the first two.

A **Force** is Needed to **Change Motion**

1) Newton's First Law says that a resultant force (p.87) is needed to make something start moving, speed up or slow down:

> If the resultant force on a stationary object is zero, the object will remain stationary. If the resultant force on a moving object is zero, it'll just carry on moving at the same velocity (the same speed and direction).

2) So, when a train or car or bus or anything else is moving at a constant velocity, the driving and resistive forces on it must be balanced.

3) Its velocity will only change if there's a non-zero resultant force acting on it.

4) A non-zero resultant force will always produce acceleration (or deceleration) in the direction of the force.

Acceleration is **Proportional** to the **Resultant Force**

1) The larger the resultant force acting on an object, the more the object accelerates.

2) Newton's Second Law says that the force acting on an object and the acceleration of the object are directly proportional. This can be shown as $F \propto a$.

3) Newton's Second Law also says that acceleration is inversely proportional to the mass of the object.

4) So an object with a larger mass will accelerate less than one with a smaller mass, for a given force.

5) There's a formula that describes Newton's Second Law:

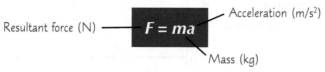

Resultant force (N) ——— **$F = ma$** ——— Acceleration (m/s²)

Mass (kg)

6) You can use Newton's Second Law to get an idea of the forces involved in large accelerations of everyday transport.

7) You may need some typical vehicle masses first though:
Car — 1000 kg, Bus — 10 000 kg, Loaded Lorry — 30 000 kg

EXAMPLE: **Estimate the resultant force on a car as it accelerates from rest to a typical speed.**

1) Estimate the speed of the car and the time taken to reach that speed.

   A typical speed of a car is ~25 m/s. It takes ~10 s to reach this.

2) Use the speed and time taken to estimate the acceleration of the car.

   So $a = \Delta v \div t = 25 \div 10 = 2.5$ m/s²

   Remember, the ~ sign means approximately.

3) Put the acceleration and the mass of the car into $F = ma$.

   Mass of a car is ~1000 kg.
   $F = ma = 1000 \times 2.5 = 2500$ N
   So the resultant force is ~2500 N.

Newton's Third Law

This page is on <u>Newton's Third Law</u>. Make sure you really understand what's going on with it.

Newton's Third Law — Interaction Pairs are Equal and Opposite

<u>Newton's Third Law</u> says:

> When <u>two objects interact</u>, the forces they exert on each other are <u>equal and opposite</u>.

1) This means if you <u>push</u> something, it will <u>push back</u> against you, <u>just as hard</u>.
2) And as soon as you <u>stop</u> pushing, <u>so does the object</u>.
3) You may be thinking "if the forces are always equal, <u>how does anything ever go anywhere</u>?".
4) The important thing to remember is that the two forces are acting on <u>different objects</u>.

Push — Normal contact force

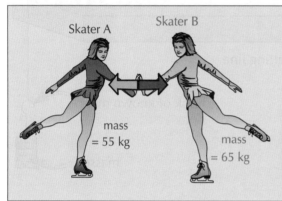

Skater A   Skater B

mass = 55 kg   mass = 65 kg

- Skater A pushes on skater B.
- When she does, she feels an <u>equal</u> and <u>opposite</u> force from skater B's hand.
- Both skaters feel the <u>same sized force</u>, in <u>opposite directions</u>.
- This causes them to accelerate away from each other.
- Skater A will be <u>accelerated more than</u> skater B, because she has a smaller mass.
- Remember <u>$a = F \div m$</u>.

It's More Complicated for an Object in Equilibrium

Imagine a <u>book</u> sat on a <u>table</u> in <u>equilibrium</u> (the <u>resultant force</u> on the book is <u>zero</u>):

1) The <u>weight</u> of the book <u>pulls</u> it <u>down</u>, and the <u>normal contact force</u> from the table <u>pushes</u> it <u>up</u>.
2) This is <u>NOT</u> Newton's Third Law.
3) These forces are <u>different types</u> and they're both <u>acting on</u> the <u>book</u>.

The <u>pairs of forces</u> due to Newton's Third Law in this case are:

- The book being <u>pulled down</u> by <u>gravity</u> towards the Earth (W_B) and the Earth being <u>pulled up</u> by the <u>book</u> (W_E).
- The <u>normal contact force</u> from the <u>table</u> pushing <u>up</u> on the book (R_B) and the <u>normal contact force</u> from the book <u>pushing down</u> on the table (R_T).

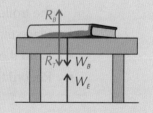

R_B

R_T W_B

W_E

Newton's Third Law is only true for interaction pairs...

Make sure you get your head around Newton's laws of motion. His <u>third law</u> can be tricky, but just take your time. Look at <u>each object</u> one at a time and work out all the <u>forces</u> acting on it before you move on.

 **Investigating Motion**

Here comes another <u>Required Practical</u>. This one's all about testing <u>Newton's Second Law</u>. It uses some nifty bits of kit that you may not have seen before, so make sure you follow the instructions closely.

You can **Investigate** how **Mass** and **Force** Affect Acceleration

This page shows you how to set up the experiment that tests <u>Newton's Second Law</u>, $F = ma$ (p.100). On the next page you can find out how to <u>investigate</u> the variables that affect Newton's Second Law.

1) Set up the <u>apparatus</u> as shown on the right.

2) The <u>mass</u>, m, that you'll be accelerating is the <u>total mass</u> of the <u>trolley</u>, <u>hook</u> and the <u>added masses</u>.

3) You can measure m using a <u>mass balance</u>.

trolley of known mass

piece of card

light gate connected to data logger (or computer)

pulley

starting line

hook of known mass

masses

4) The <u>force</u>, F, causing the acceleration is the <u>weight</u> of the <u>hook and the masses on the hook</u>.

5) To find F, first measure the <u>mass</u> of the <u>hook</u> and any masses <u>on the hook</u>. Then <u>multiply this by g</u> (as $W = mg$, see page 86).

6) The <u>acceleration</u>, a, is found by following this method:

For more on how light gates work have a look at page 134.

- Mark a <u>starting line</u> on the table the trolley is on. This is so that the trolley always travels the <u>same distance</u> to the light gate.
- Place the trolley on the <u>starting line</u>.
- Hold the trolley so the string is <u>tight</u> and not touching the table. Then <u>release</u> it.
- Record the <u>acceleration</u> measured by the light gate as the trolley passes through it.

This experiment has a lot of steps, so don't speed through it...

Make sure the <u>string</u> is the <u>right length</u> and there's <u>enough space</u> for the hanging masses to <u>fall</u>. There needs to be enough space so that the masses <u>don't</u> hit the floor <u>before</u> the trolley has <u>passed through the light gate fully</u> — if they hit the floor, the force won't be applied the whole way through the trolley's journey, so you won't get an accurate measurement for the <u>acceleration</u>.

Investigating Motion

Now you know how to set up the <u>equipment</u> (p.102) it's time to start looking at <u>adjusting</u> your <u>variables</u>. Take care with the <u>method</u> here — there are some important points you don't want to miss.

Investigating How **Mass** Affects **Acceleration**

To investigate the effect of mass, you need to <u>change the mass</u> but keep the force <u>the same</u>. Remember, the <u>mass</u> (m) is the mass of the trolley, the hook and any extra masses <u>added together</u>.

1) The force is the <u>weight</u> of the <u>hook and any masses on the hook.</u>

2) So, keep the mass <u>on the hook</u> the <u>same</u>.

3) <u>Add masses</u> to the <u>trolley</u> one at a time to increase the <u>total mass</u> being accelerated.

4) Record the <u>acceleration</u>, a, for <u>each total mass</u>, m.

5) You should find that as the mass <u>goes up</u>, the acceleration <u>goes down</u>.

6) This <u>agrees</u> with Newton's Second Law — mass and acceleration are <u>inversely proportional</u>.

Investigating How **Force** Affects **Acceleration**

This time, you need to <u>change</u> the force <u>without changing</u> the <u>total mass</u> of the trolley, hook and masses.

1) Start with <u>all</u> the extra masses loaded onto the <u>trolley</u>.

2) Moving the masses <u>from</u> the trolley to the hook will keep the <u>total mass</u>, m, the same.

3) But it will <u>increase</u> the force, F (the <u>weight</u> of the <u>hook and the masses on the hook</u>).

4) <u>Each time</u> you <u>move</u> a mass, record the <u>new force</u>, and measure the <u>acceleration</u>.

5) You should find that as the force <u>goes up</u>, the acceleration <u>goes up</u>.

6) This <u>agrees</u> with Newton's Second Law — force and acceleration are <u>directly proportional</u>.

Warm-Up & Exam Questions

Now you've gotten yourself on the right side of the law(s) of motion), it's time to put your knowledge on trial. Have a go at the warm-up questions first and then knuckle down to those exam questions.

Warm-Up Questions

1) True or false? The resultant force acting on an accelerating object must have a magnitude greater than zero.

2) Boulders A and B are accelerated at 2 m/s². Boulder A required a force of 70 N, and Boulder B required a force of 95 N. Which boulder has a greater mass?

3) True or false? Two interacting objects exert equal and opposite forces on each other.

Exam Questions

1   A ball hits a stationary cricket bat. The bat exerts a force of 520 N on the ball when they are in contact. The cricket bat has a mass of 1.6 kg and the ball has a mass of 160 g.   *(Grade 3-4)*

1.1   State the force that the ball exerts on the bat.

[1 mark]

1.2   Complete the sentence below using words from the box.

| less than | the same as | greater than |

The acceleration of the ball will be .... that of the bat because it has a smaller mass.

[1 mark]

1.3   Use the following formula to calculate the size of the acceleration of the bat when the ball hits it.
Force = mass × acceleration

[3 marks]

2   The camper van shown in **Figure 1** has a mass of 2500 kg. It is driven along a straight, level road at a constant speed of 90.0 kilometres per hour.   *(Grade 4-5)*

Figure 1

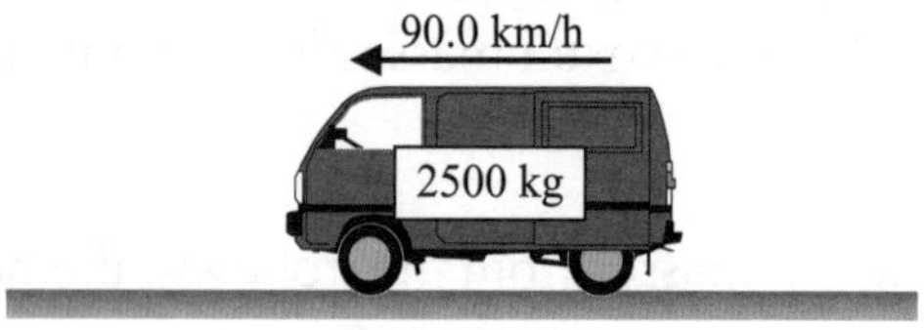

90.0 km/h

2500 kg

2.1   State the resultant force acting on the camper van.

[1 mark]

2.2   The camper van slows down. What changes from those below could have caused the van to slow down? Tick **two** boxes.

☐ The driving force decreases

☐ The wind blowing in the opposite direction to the van's movement increases

☐ The drag acting on the van decreases

☐ The van becomes lighter

[2 marks]

2.3   The camper van slows down with a deceleration of 1.4 m/s². What is the resultant force acting on the van during its deceleration? Give the direction of the resultant force.

[3 marks]

Topic 5 — Forces

Stopping Distance and Thinking Distance

This page is all about cars, but unfortunately it's not as fun as it sounds... It's even better — it's about safety...

Stopping Distance = Thinking Distance + Braking Distance

1) In an emergency, a driver may perform an emergency stop.
2) During an emergency stop, the maximum force is applied by the brakes.
   This is so the vehicle stops in the shortest possible distance.
3) The distance it takes to stop a vehicle in an emergency is its stopping distance. It is found by:

> Stopping Distance = Thinking Distance + Braking Distance

4) Thinking distance is how far the vehicle travels during the driver's reaction time.
5) The reaction time is the time between the driver seeing a hazard and applying the brakes.
6) Braking distance is the distance taken to stop under the braking force (once the brakes are applied).

Stopping Distances for Different Speeds can be Estimated

1) You need to be able to estimate the stopping distance of vehicles.
2) The heavier a vehicle is, or the faster it's travelling, the longer its stopping distance will be.
3) As a guide, typical car stopping distances are: 23 m at 30 mph, 73 m at 60 mph, 96 m at 70 mph.

Stopping Distances Affect Safety

1) The longer it takes to perform an emergency stop, the higher the risk of crashing into whatever's in front.
2) So the shorter a vehicle's stopping distance, the safer it is.
3) You need to be able to describe how different factors can affect the safety of a journey.
4) For example, how driving if you're tired is unsafe. There's more on this below.

Thinking Distance is Determined by the Driver's Reactions

1) Thinking distance is affected by:

   - Your speed — the faster you're going, the further you'll travel during the time you take to react.
   - Your reaction time — the longer your reaction time (p.107), the longer your thinking distance.

2) A driver's reaction times can be affected by tiredness, drugs or alcohol.
3) Distractions can also affect your ability to react.

   - Driving while tired is unsafe as it makes you slower to react.
   - This increases your reaction time, which increases your thinking distance.
   - This means your stopping distance is longer, so you're more likely to crash.

   - Driving above the speed limit is unsafe.
   - You travel further in your reaction time than you would at a lower speed.
   - This increases your thinking (and so stopping) distance.

Braking Distance

So you know the basics of <u>stopping distances</u> now, but how do the brakes actually work to <u>slow down a car</u>? Well, it's all down to <u>friction</u> and <u>transferring energy</u> away from the wheels to the brakes.

Braking Distance Depends on a Few Different Factors

<u>Braking distance</u> is affected by:

1) Your <u>speed</u>: for a <u>given</u> braking force, the <u>faster</u> a vehicle travels, the <u>longer</u> it takes to stop.
2) <u>Weather</u> or <u>road surface</u>:
   - If there is less <u>grip</u> between a vehicle's tyres and the road, it can cause the vehicle to <u>skid</u>.
   - <u>Skidding</u> increases the <u>braking distance</u> of a car.
   - <u>Water</u>, <u>ice</u>, <u>oil</u> or <u>leaves</u> on the road all reduce grip.

   > Icy conditions increase the <u>chance of skidding</u>. This increases the <u>braking distance</u>, which increases the <u>stopping distance</u>. So <u>more room</u> should be left between cars to be <u>safe</u>.

3) The <u>condition</u> of your <u>tyres</u>:
   - <u>Bald tyres</u> (ones that don't have <u>any tread left</u>) cannot <u>get rid of water</u> in wet conditions.
   - This leads to them <u>skidding</u> on top of the water.
4) How good your <u>brakes</u> are:
   - If brakes are <u>worn</u>, they won't be able to apply as much <u>force</u>.
   - So it takes <u>longer</u> to stop a vehicle travelling at a <u>given speed</u> (see below).

Braking Relies on Friction Between the Brakes and Wheels

1) When the brake pedal is pushed, brake pads are <u>pressed</u> onto the wheels.
2) The brake pads cause <u>friction</u>, which <u>causes work to be done</u> (p.87).
3) Remember, when <u>work is done</u>, energy is <u>transferred</u> (p.20).
4) <u>Energy</u> is transferred from the <u>kinetic energy store</u> of the vehicle to the <u>thermal energy stores</u> of the <u>brakes</u>.
5) The brakes <u>increase</u> in <u>temperature</u>.
6) To <u>stop</u> a vehicle, the brakes must transfer <u>all</u> of the energy from the <u>kinetic store</u>, so:

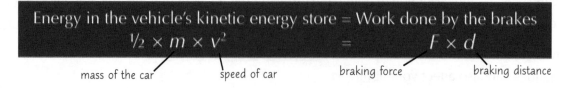

Energy in the vehicle's kinetic energy store = Work done by the brakes
$$\tfrac{1}{2} \times m \times v^2 \qquad = \qquad F \times d$$

mass of the car   speed of car   braking force   braking distance

7) The <u>faster</u> a vehicle is going, the more energy it has in its <u>kinetic</u> energy store.
8) So more <u>work</u> needs to be done to stop it.
9) This means that as the speed of a vehicle <u>increases</u>, the force needed to make it stop within a certain distance also <u>increases</u>.
10) A larger <u>braking force</u> means a larger <u>deceleration</u>.
11) <u>Very large decelerations</u> can be <u>dangerous</u> because they may cause brakes to <u>overheat</u>. This means the brakes won't work as well.
12) Very large decelerations may also cause the vehicle to <u>skid</u>.

Reaction Times

Reaction times are an <u>important factor</u> in <u>thinking distances</u>. They're also super easy to <u>test</u> for yourself. Read on for a simple <u>experiment</u> you can do in the lab.

A Typical **Reaction Time** is **0.2 s – 0.9 s**

1) <u>Everyone's</u> reaction time is <u>different</u>.

2) A <u>typical</u> reaction time is between <u>0.2</u> and <u>0.9 s</u>.

3) You can do <u>simple experiments</u> to investigate your reaction time — more on these below.

You can **Measure** Reaction Times with the **Ruler Drop Test**

1) As reaction times are <u>so short</u>, you haven't got a chance of measuring one with a <u>stopwatch</u>.

2) One way of measuring reaction times is to use a <u>computer-based test</u>. For example, <u>clicking a mouse</u> when the screen changes colour.

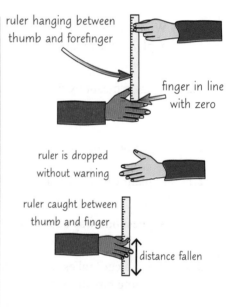

ruler hanging between thumb and forefinger

finger in line with zero

ruler is dropped without warning

ruler caught between thumb and finger

distance fallen

Another method to measure reaction times is the <u>ruler drop test</u>:

1) Sit with your arm resting on the edge of a table.

2) Get someone else to hold a ruler so it <u>hangs between</u> your thumb and forefinger, lined up with <u>zero</u>.

3) You may need a <u>third person</u> to be at <u>eye level</u> <u>with the ruler</u> to check it's lined up.

4) Without giving any warning, the person holding the ruler should <u>drop it</u>.

5) Close your thumb and finger to try to <u>catch</u> <u>the ruler as quickly as possible</u>.

6) The measurement on the ruler at the point where it is caught is <u>how far</u> the ruler dropped in the time it took you to react.

7) The <u>longer</u> the <u>distance</u>, the <u>longer</u> the <u>reaction time</u>.

8) You can calculate <u>how long</u> the ruler falls for (the <u>reaction</u> time) because <u>acceleration due to gravity is constant</u>.

9) To find the <u>reaction time</u>, you'll need to use the equation:

You <u>don't</u> need to learn this equation. It comes from squishing $v^2 - u^2 = 2as$ and $a = \Delta v \div t$ from p.95 together.

$$t = \frac{\sqrt{2as}}{a}$$

t is the <u>reaction time</u> in seconds, s.

a is the <u>acceleration due to gravity</u>. $a = 9.8$ m/s².

s is <u>how far</u> the ruler fell before it was caught, in metres, m.

It's <u>hard</u> to do this experiment <u>accurately</u>, but you can do a few things to <u>improve</u> your <u>results</u>.

• Do a lot of <u>repeats</u> and calculate an <u>average</u> reaction time.

• Add a <u>blob of modelling clay</u> to the bottom to help the ruler to fall straight down.

• Make it a <u>fair test</u> — use the <u>same ruler</u> for each repeat, and have the <u>same person</u> dropping it.

Take steps to improve the validity of your results...

You may get asked to suggest <u>improvements</u> to <u>methods</u> used in an experiment. E.g. in the one above you need to look for things like: did they use the same ruler each time to make it a fair test?

Warm-Up & Exam Questions

Time to apply the brakes for a second and put your brain through its paces. Try out these questions.
If you can handle these, your exam should be clear of hazards.

1) Give one factor that can affect thinking distance.
2) What must be added to the thinking distance to find the total stopping distance of a car?
3) Give one reason that the large deceleration of a car can be dangerous.
4) True or false? The larger the braking force, the greater the deceleration of a car.

Exam Question

1   The stopping distance of a car is the distance covered in the time between the driver first spotting a hazard and the car coming to a complete stop.   *Grade 1-3*

1.1   What name is given to the distance travelled between the driver first spotting a hazard and then applying the brakes?

[1 mark]

1.2   What is meant by the braking distance of a car?

[1 mark]

2   A person is driving a car in heavy rain.   *Grade 3-4*

2.1   Explain why heavy rain increases a car's stopping distance.

[1 mark]

2.2   Suggest **one** way a driver can decrease their stopping distance when driving in heavy rain.

[1 mark]

2.3   When a car brakes, work is done. What energy transfer occurs?
Tick **one** box in each row.

	The car's kinetic energy stores	The car's chemical energy stores	The brakes' thermal energy stores	The brakes' elastic energy stores
Energy transferred from	☐	☐	☐	☐
Energy transferred to	☐	☐	☐	☐

[2 marks]

3   A student tries to catch a falling ruler as quickly as possible.
The distance the ruler falls can be used to calculate the student's reaction time.
The student repeats the test three times. Their results are shown below.   *Grade 4-5*

0.24 s   0.19 s   0.23 s

3.1   Calculate the student's mean reaction time.

[2 marks]

3.2   State **one** way the student could improve their results.

[1 mark]

Revision Summary for Topic 5

Well, that's <u>Topic 5</u> over and done with — have a quick break, then see how you've done with this summary.

- Try these questions and <u>tick off each one</u> when you <u>get it right</u>.
- When you've done <u>all the questions</u> under a heading and are <u>completely happy</u> with it, tick it off.

Forces and Work Done (p.85-87) ☐

1) Explain the difference between scalar and vector quantities.
2) True or false? Time is a vector quantity.
3) What is the difference between contact and non-contact forces?
4) True or false? Mass is a force measured in newtons.
5) What is the formula for calculating the weight of an object?
6) What is a resultant force?
7) Why does the temperature of an object increase when it is pushed along a rough surface?
8) How many joules of work does 1 Nm equal?

Elasticity and Springs (p.89-92) ☑

9) What is the difference between an elastic and an inelastic deformation?
10) What is the limit of proportionality?
11) Sketch a typical force-extension graph for a spring where its limit of proportionality is exceeded.
12) Describe an experiment you could do to investigate the relationship between force and extension.

Motion (p.94-98) ☐

13) What is the difference between displacement and distance?
14) Estimate the speed of a person walking.
15) Write down the equation that links acceleration, velocity and time.
16) For what type of acceleration can you use the equation $v^2 - u^2 = 2as$?
17) What does the gradient represent for: a) a distance-time graph? b) a velocity-time graph?

Newton's Laws of Motion (p.100-103) ☐

18) State Newton's three laws of motion.
19) Describe an experiment that you could do to investigate Newton's Second Law.

Car Safety (p.105-107) ☐

20) What is the stopping distance of a vehicle? How can it be calculated?
21) What is a typical stopping distance of a car travelling at 60 mph?
22) Give two things that affect a person's reaction time.
23) What is a typical reaction time?
24) Briefly describe an experiment you could do to compare people's reaction times.

Wave Basics

Waves <u>transfer energy</u> from one place to another <u>without</u> transferring any <u>matter</u> (stuff).

Waves Transfer **Energy** but not **Matter**

1) When a wave <u>travels through</u> a medium, the particles of the <u>medium</u> vibrate.
2) A <u>medium</u> is just a fancy word for whatever the wave is <u>travelling through</u> (e.g. water, air).
3) The particles <u>transfer energy</u> between each other as they vibrate (see p.19).
4) <u>BUT</u> overall, the particles stay in the <u>same place</u> — <u>only energy</u> is transferred.

- For example, if you drop a twig into calm water, <u>ripples</u> spread out.
  The ripples <u>don't</u> carry the <u>water</u> (or the twig) away with them though.
- And if you strum a <u>guitar string</u>, the sound waves don't carry the <u>air</u> away
  from the guitar. If they did, you'd feel a <u>wind</u> whenever there was a sound.

Waves have an **Amplitude**, **Wavelength** and **Frequency**

1) The <u>amplitude</u> of a wave is the <u>maximum displacement</u>
   of a point on the wave from its <u>undisturbed (rest) position</u>.

2) The <u>wavelength</u> is the distance between <u>one point</u> on a wave and the
   <u>same point</u> on the <u>next wave</u>. For example, the distance between the
   <u>trough</u> of one wave and the <u>trough</u> of the wave <u>next to it</u>.

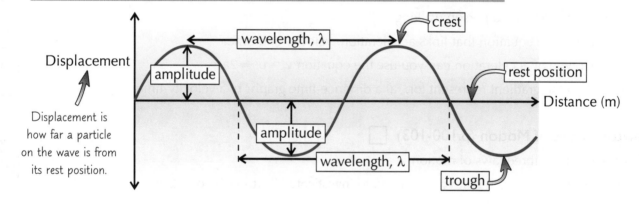

Displacement is
how far a particle
on the wave is from
its rest position.

3) <u>Frequency</u> is the <u>number of complete waves</u> passing a certain point <u>each second</u>.
   Frequency is measured in <u>hertz</u> (Hz). 1 Hz is <u>1 wave per second</u>.

4) <u>Period</u> is the amount of <u>time</u> it takes for <u>one</u> complete wave to <u>pass</u> a certain point.

The only thing a wave transfers is energy...

It's <u>really</u> important that you understand this stuff <u>really</u> well, or the rest of this topic will be a blur.
Make sure you can sketch the <u>wave diagram</u> above and can <u>label</u> all the features from memory.

Transverse and Longitudinal Waves

All waves are either <u>transverse</u> or <u>longitudinal</u>. Read on to find out more...

Transverse Waves Have **Perpendicular** Vibrations

1) In <u>transverse waves</u>, the vibrations are <u>perpendicular</u> (at right angles) to the <u>direction</u> of energy transfer.
2) <u>Examples</u> of transverse waves are <u>light</u> (p.117), <u>ripples</u> on water (see p.113) and waves on a <u>string</u> (p.114).
3) A spring wiggled <u>up and down</u> gives a <u>transverse wave</u>:

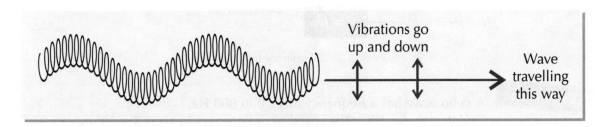

Vibrations go up and down

Wave travelling this way

Longitudinal Waves Have **Parallel** Vibrations

1) In <u>longitudinal waves</u>, the vibrations are in the <u>same direction</u> as the energy transfer.
2) They have <u>compressions</u> (where the particles squish together), and <u>rarefactions</u> (where they spread out).
3) A <u>sound wave</u> is an <u>example</u> of a longitudinal wave.
4) If you <u>push</u> the end of a spring, you get a <u>longitudinal wave</u>:

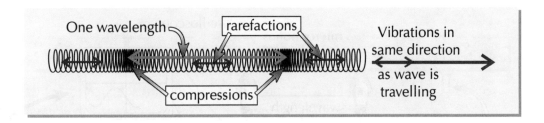

One wavelength rarefactions

Vibrations in same direction as wave is travelling

compressions

Frequency and Period are Linked

You can find the <u>period</u> of a wave from its <u>frequency</u>:

Period (s) — $T = \dfrac{1}{f}$ — Frequency (Hz)

EXAMPLE:

Calculate the period of a wave with a frequency of 2 Hz.

$T = 1 \div f = 1 \div 2 = 0.5$ s

Light waves are transverse and sound waves are longitudinal...

The equation that links <u>period</u> and <u>frequency</u> together is pretty useful — it means that you can always work one out from the other. Make sure you <u>practise</u> using the equation until you're comfortable with it.

Wave Speed

Measuring the speed of waves isn't that simple. It calls for crafty methods...

Wave Speed = Frequency × Wavelength

1) The wave speed is how fast the wave is moving.
2) It is the speed at which energy is being transferred through the medium.
3) The wave equation applies to all waves:

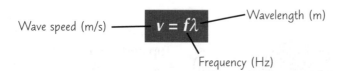

Wave speed (m/s) — $v = f\lambda$ — Wavelength (m)

Frequency (Hz)

EXAMPLE: **A radio wave has a frequency of 12 000 000 Hz.
Find its wavelength. (The speed of radio waves in air is 3 × 10⁸ m/s.)**

1) Rearrange the wave speed equation for wavelength. $\lambda = v \div f$
2) Put in the values you've been given. $= (3 \times 10^8) \div (12\ 000\ 000)$
   Watch out — the speed is in standard form (p.12). $= 25\ m$

Use an Oscilloscope to Measure the Speed of Sound

1) Connect two microphones to an oscilloscope (a device which shows waves on a screen).
2) Connect a signal generator to a speaker. This will let you generate sound waves at a set frequency.

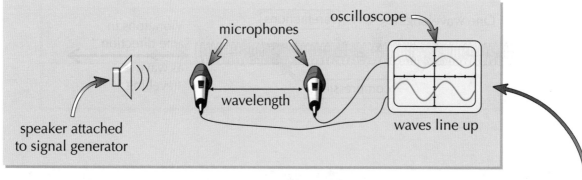

3) Set up the oscilloscope so the waves reaching each microphone are shown separately.
4) Start with both microphones next to the speaker. The waves on the oscilloscope should line up.
5) Slowly move one microphone away. Stop when the two waves line up again on the display.
6) This means the microphones are now exactly one wavelength apart.
7) Measure the distance between the microphones to find the wavelength (λ).
8) Use the formula $v = f\lambda$ to find the speed (v) of the sound waves passing through the air.
9) The frequency (f) is whatever you set the signal generator to.
10) The speed of sound in air is around 330 m/s, so check your results roughly agree with this.

That was the first of three wave speed practicals to learn...

Make sure you understand each step of that method above — you could be tested on it in the exams.

Investigating Waves

Choosing <u>suitable equipment</u> means making sure it's <u>right</u> for the job. It's important here.

Measure the **Speed** of **Water Ripples** Using a **Ripple Tank**

1) Attach a <u>signal generator</u> to the <u>ripple tank dipper</u>. Turn on the signal generator to create <u>waves</u>.

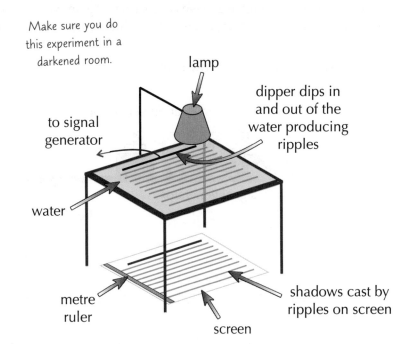

Make sure you do this experiment in a darkened room.

lamp

dipper dips in and out of the water producing ripples

to signal generator

water

metre ruler

screen

shadows cast by ripples on screen

2) Find the <u>frequency</u> of the waves by <u>counting</u> the number of <u>ripples</u> that pass a point in 10 seconds and <u>dividing by 10</u>.

3) Use a <u>lamp</u> to create <u>shadows</u> of the ripples on a screen below the tank. Place a <u>metre ruler</u> beside the shadows.

4) The distance between each shadow line is equal to <u>one wavelength</u>.

5) Measure the wavelength <u>accurately</u> by measuring the <u>distance</u> across <u>10 gaps</u> between the shadow lines. <u>Divide</u> this distance <u>by 10</u> to find the <u>average wavelength</u>.

This is a good method for measuring the wavelength of moving waves or small wavelengths.

6) If you're struggling to measure the distance, you could take a <u>photo</u> of the <u>shadows and ruler</u>, and find the wavelength from the photo instead.

7) Use $v = f\lambda$ to calculate the wave <u>speed</u> of the waves.

8) This set-up is <u>suitable</u> for investigating waves, because it allows you to <u>measure</u> the wavelength without <u>disturbing</u> the waves.

Make sure your measurements are accurate...

You should be careful that the <u>screen</u> beneath the tank is <u>flat</u>, or the shadows will become distorted and difficult to measure properly. You should also make sure that the metre <u>ruler</u> is at a <u>right angle</u> to the shadow wavefronts — if the ruler is skewed then your measured wavelength will be too long.

Investigating Waves

One more <u>wave experiment</u> coming up. This time, it's to do with <u>waves on strings</u>.

You can Use the **Wave Equation** for Waves on **Strings**

In this practical, you create a wave on a string. Again, you use a <u>signal generator</u>, but this time you attach it to a <u>vibration generator</u> which converts the signals to vibrations.

1) Set up the equipment shown below.

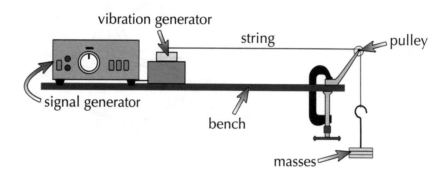

vibration generator

string

pulley

signal generator

bench

masses

2) The <u>vibration generator vibrates</u> at a <u>fixed frequency</u>, set by the signal generator.

3) <u>Turn on</u> the signal generator and the string will start to <u>vibrate</u>.

4) Adjust the <u>frequency</u> of the signal generator until there's a <u>clear wave</u> on the string.

5) To measure the <u>wavelength</u> of these waves accurately:
   - Count <u>how many</u> wavelengths are on the string. Each <u>vibrating loop</u> is <u>half a wavelength</u>.
   - Measure the <u>length</u> of the <u>whole</u> vibrating string.
   - <u>Divide</u> by the number of <u>wavelengths</u> to give the length of <u>one wavelength</u>.

measure this distance

there are 2 wavelengths on the string, so divide the distance by 2

6) The <u>frequency</u> of the wave is whatever the <u>signal generator</u> is set to.

It's ok if you don't have a whole number of wavelengths on the string. If there are 3 loops, there are one-and-a-half wavelengths on the string. Divide the length of the string by 1.5.

7) You can find the <u>speed</u> of the wave using $v = f\lambda$.

8) This set-up is <u>suitable</u> for investigating waves on a string because it's easy to <u>see</u> and <u>measure</u> the wavelength (and frequency).

PRACTICAL TIP

Learn the methods for all the wave speed practicals...

The experiments on pages 112-114 seem complicated, but they all have a few things <u>in common</u>. First, you set the <u>frequency</u> on the signal generator, then find the length of the resulting wave (this tends to be the fiddly bit). You can then use the <u>equation</u> $v = f\lambda$ to find the <u>wave speed</u>.

Refraction

Grab a glass of water and put a straw in it. The straw looks like it's <u>bending</u>. But it's not magic, it's refraction.

Refraction — Waves **Changing Direction**

1) When a wave crosses a <u>boundary</u> between two materials it can change direction.

2) This is known as <u>refraction</u>.

3) Waves are <u>only refracted</u> if they meet the boundary <u>at an angle</u>.

4) <u>How much</u> a wave is refracted by depends on the two materials it's passing between.

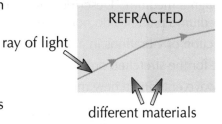

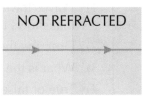

Ray Diagrams Show the **Path** of a **Wave**

- Rays are <u>straight lines</u> that show the <u>direction</u> a wave is <u>travelling</u> in.
- You can construct a <u>ray diagram</u> for a <u>refracted light ray</u>.

1) Start by drawing the <u>boundary</u> between your two materials.

2) Then draw a dotted line <u>at right angles</u> to the boundary.

3) This line is known as the '<u>normal</u>' to the boundary. Normal just means 'at right angles'.

4) Next draw the <u>incident ray</u>. This is the ray that <u>meets</u> the <u>boundary</u> at the <u>normal</u>.

5) The angle <u>between</u> the incident <u>ray</u> and the <u>normal</u> is called the <u>angle of incidence</u>.

6) You need to use a <u>protractor</u> to draw or measure it.

7) So to draw an incident ray with an <u>angle of incidence</u> of <u>50°</u>:

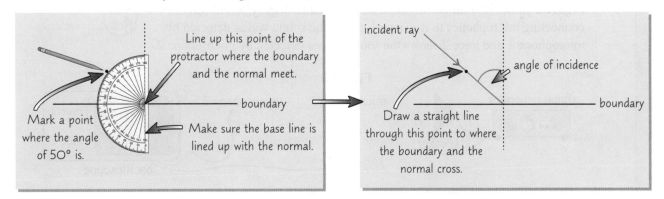

8) Now draw the <u>refracted</u> ray on the <u>other side</u> of the boundary.

9) <u>The angle of refraction</u> is the angle between the <u>refracted ray</u> and the normal.

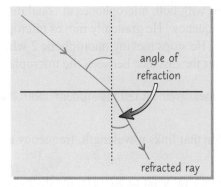

Hitting a boundary at an angle leads to refraction...

Refraction is a common behaviour of waves, so make sure you really <u>understand</u> it before moving on.

Warm-Up & Exam Questions

Now to check what's actually stuck in your mind over the last few pages...

Exam Questions

1 **Figure 1** shows a graph of a water wave.

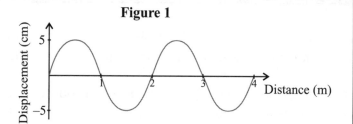

Figure 1

1.1 Give **one** reason why water waves are classified as transverse waves rather than longitudinal waves.

[1 mark]

1.2 Give the amplitude of this wave.

[1 mark]

1.3 Give the wavelength of this wave.

[1 mark]

2 **Figure 2** shows how an oscilloscope can be used to display sound waves by connecting microphones to it. Trace 1 shows the sound waves detected by microphone 1 and trace 2 shows the sound waves detected by microphone 2.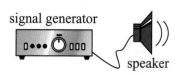

Figure 2

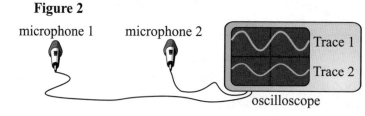

A student begins with both microphones at equal distances from the speaker and the signal generator set at a fixed frequency. He gradually moves microphone 2 away from the speaker, which causes trace 2 to move. He stops moving microphone 2 when both traces line up again as shown in **Figure 2**. He then measures the distance between the microphones.

2.1 What does this measurement tell the student about the sound waves detected?

[1 mark]

2.2 Give the equation that links wavelength, frequency and wave speed.

[1 mark]

2.3 With the signal generator set to 50.0 Hz, the distance between the microphones was measured as 6.8 m. Calculate the speed of sound in air. Give the correct unit.

[3 marks]

Electromagnetic Waves

The <u>light waves</u> that we see are just one small part of a big group of <u>electromagnetic waves</u>...

Electromagnetic Waves Transfer Energy

1) <u>Electromagnetic</u> (<u>EM</u>) <u>waves</u> are <u>transverse</u> waves (p.111).

2) They transfer energy <u>from a source</u> to an <u>absorber</u>.

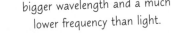

- A <u>camp fire</u> is a source.
- It <u>transfers energy</u> to its surroundings by giving out <u>infrared</u> radiation.
- Infrared radiation is a type of <u>EM wave</u>.
- These infrared waves are <u>absorbed</u> by objects.
- Energy is transferred to the objects' <u>thermal energy stores</u>.
- This causes the objects to <u>warm up</u>.

3) All EM waves travel at the <u>same speed</u> through <u>air</u> or a <u>vacuum</u> (<u>space</u>).

4) This speed is <u>much faster</u> than the speed of sound in air.

Sound waves have a much bigger wavelength and a much lower frequency than light.

There's a Continuous Spectrum of EM Waves

1) EM waves vary in <u>wavelength</u> and <u>frequency</u>.

2) There are EM waves of <u>every</u> wavelength within a certain <u>range</u>.

3) This is known as a <u>continuous spectrum</u>.

4) The spectrum is split up into seven groups based on <u>wavelength</u> and <u>frequency</u>.

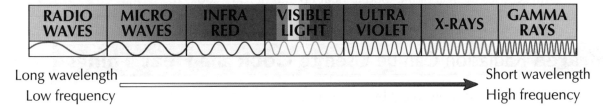

RADIO WAVES	MICRO WAVES	INFRA RED	VISIBLE LIGHT	ULTRA VIOLET	X-RAYS	GAMMA RAYS

Long wavelength
Low frequency

Short wavelength
High frequency

5) Our <u>eyes</u> can only detect a <u>small part</u> of this spectrum — <u>visible light</u>.

Changes In Atoms Produce the Spectrum of EM Waves

1) <u>EM radiation</u> can be <u>absorbed</u> or <u>produced</u> by changes in atoms and their nuclei.

2) There are lots of <u>different</u> changes that can happen in atoms. For example:
   - Electrons can move between <u>energy levels</u> in atoms (see p.73).
   - Changes in the <u>nucleus</u> of an atom can create <u>gamma rays</u> (see p.77).

3) Each different change <u>produces</u> or <u>absorbs</u> a different frequency of <u>EM wave</u>.

4) This is why atoms can <u>generate</u> (create) EM waves over a large <u>range of frequencies</u>.

5) It is also why atoms can <u>absorb</u> a range of frequencies.

Study the EM spectrum and wave goodbye to exam stress...

There are a lot of <u>facts</u> to remember here, and you need to know them all. Here's a handy way to remember the <u>order</u> of EM waves: 'Rock Music Is Very Useful for eXperience with Guitars'.

Uses of EM Waves

EM waves are used for all sorts of stuff — and <u>radio waves</u> are definitely the most fun.
They make your car <u>radio</u> and your <u>TV</u> work. Life would be pretty quiet without them.

Radio Waves are Used Mainly for Communication

1) <u>Radio</u> and <u>TV</u> signals can be sent by radio waves.

2) <u>Very short wavelength</u> signals are used for FM radio and TV.

3) They have to be <u>in direct sight</u> of the receiver when they're sent, with nothing in the way, so they <u>can't</u> travel <u>very far</u>.

4) <u>Longer wavelength</u> radio waves can travel further.

5) They can be used to send radio signals <u>around the world</u>.

Microwaves are Used for Satellites and Cooking

1) Communication with <u>satellites</u> uses microwaves, e.g. for <u>satellite TV</u> and <u>satellite phones</u>.
   - A signal is sent into space to a satellite dish <u>high</u> above the Earth.
   - The satellite <u>sends</u> the signal back to Earth in a different direction.
   - A <u>satellite dish</u> on the ground receives the signal.

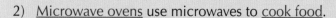

2) <u>Microwave ovens</u> use microwaves to <u>cook food</u>.
   - The oven gives out microwaves, which are <u>absorbed</u> by <u>water</u> in the food.
   - <u>Energy carried</u> by the microwaves is <u>transferred to</u> the water molecules, causing them to heat up.
   - This causes the rest of the <u>food</u> to heat up and quickly <u>cooks</u> it.

Infrared Radiation Can be Used to Cook and Heat Things

1) <u>Infrared</u> (IR) radiation is <u>given out</u> by all <u>objects</u>.

2) The <u>hotter</u> the object, the <u>more</u> infrared radiation it gives out.

3) When an object <u>absorbs</u> infrared radiation, <u>energy is transferred</u> to the object's <u>thermal energy store</u>. This makes it <u>warm up</u>.

4) Infrared radiation can be <u>used</u> in many ways:

   - <u>Infrared cameras</u> detect IR radiation and create a <u>picture</u>.
   - This is useful for seeing where a house is <u>losing energy</u>.
   - It can also allow you to see <u>hot objects</u> in the <u>dark</u>.

The different colours mean different amounts of IR radiation are being detected from those areas. Here, the redder the colour, the more infrared radiation is being detected.

   - Infrared radiation can also be used to <u>warm things</u>.
   - <u>Electric heaters</u> release lots of IR radiation to warm a room.
   - And <u>food</u> can be <u>cooked</u> using infrared radiation.

The uses of EM waves depend on their properties...

Differences in wavelength, frequency and energy between types of EM wave give them <u>different properties</u>. For example, some types of EM wave are <u>very harmful</u> (see page 122). Luckily, radio waves are considered <u>safe</u> to beam round the world. IR radiation is generally fairly safe, although too much of it will burn you.

More Uses of EM Waves

And we're still not finished with uses of EM waves — there's just no end to their talents...

Fibre Optic Cables Use Visible Light to Send Data

1) Optical fibres are thin glass or plastic tubes that can carry data over long distances.
2) They're often used to send information to telephones or computers.
3) Information is sent as light rays that bounce back and forth along the fibre.

Glass fibre

Light ray

Ultraviolet Radiation Gives You a Suntan

1) When some materials absorb UV light, they give off visible light.
2) This can be pretty useful:

- Energy-efficient lights use UV radiation to produce visible light.
- Security pens can be used to mark property with your name (e.g. laptops).
- Under UV light the ink will glow, but it's invisible otherwise.
- This can help the police find out who stolen property belongs to.

3) Ultraviolet radiation (UV) is also produced by the Sun. It's what gives you a suntan.
4) UV lamps can be used to give people a suntan without the Sun (but this can be dangerous).

X-rays and Gamma Rays are Used in Medicine

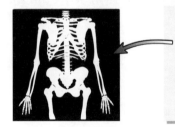

1) X-rays pass easily through flesh but not through bones or metal.
2) This can be used to create an X-ray image to check for broken bones.
3) X-rays can also treat people with cancer.
4) This is because they can kill cells.
   They are aimed at the cancer cells to kill them.

1) Gamma rays (p.77) can also kill cells.
2) They can be used to treat cancer in the same way as X-rays.
3) They can also be used to sterilise (remove germs from) medical equipment.
   The equipment is blasted with gamma rays which kills any living things on it.
4) Gamma rays are also really good at passing through your body.
5) This is why small amounts of them are used in 'medical tracers'.
   How they move around the body can be tracked.
   This can tell doctors if organs are working as they should.

Communications, security and imaging — pretty important stuff...

I hate to say it, but go back to page 118 and read all of the uses for EM waves again to really learn them.

 **Investigating IR Radiation**

Time for another <u>Required Practical</u>. In this one, you'll meet a fun, new piece of kit called a <u>Leslie cube</u>. Read on to find out more about how you can use this equipment to investigate <u>infrared radiation emissions</u>.

Different Surfaces Emit Different Amounts of IR Radiation

1) The amount of <u>infrared radiation</u> an object gives out depends on its <u>temperature</u> — see p.118.

2) It also depends on its <u>surface</u>.

3) This includes how <u>rough</u> or <u>shiny</u> it is, and its <u>colour</u>.

4) You can investigate <u>how much</u> IR radiation different surfaces emit using a <u>Leslie cube</u>.

5) A <u>Leslie cube</u> is a <u>hollow</u>, metal cube.

6) The <u>four side faces</u> have <u>different surfaces</u>.

7) For example, <u>matt</u> (dull) <u>black paint</u>, matt <u>white paint</u>, <u>shiny</u> metal and <u>dull</u> metal.

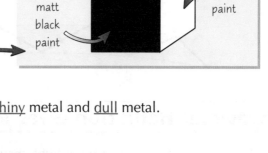

matt white paint

matt black paint

You Can Investigate Emission With a Leslie Cube

1) Place an <u>empty Leslie cube</u> on a <u>heat-proof</u> mat. <u>Draw</u> a square around the cube that is 10 cm from <u>all faces</u> of the cube.

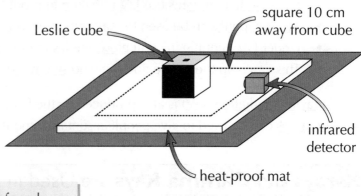

Leslie cube

square 10 cm away from cube

infrared detector

heat-proof mat

2) <u>Fill</u> the Leslie cube with boiling water and wait for the cube to <u>warm up</u>.

3) Use the square you've drawn to hold an <u>infrared detector</u> 10 cm away from one of the cube's vertical faces. Record the <u>amount of IR radiation</u> it detects.

4) <u>Repeat</u> step 3) for <u>each</u> of the <u>four faces</u>.

5) The face that had the <u>highest reading</u> is giving off the most IR radiation.

6) You should find that the <u>black</u> surface is radiating more IR radiation than the <u>white</u> one. <u>Matt</u> surfaces should give off more than <u>shiny</u> ones.

7) As always, you should <u>repeat</u> the experiment to check your <u>results</u>.

You can feel which face is giving off the most heat...

When doing this experiment, you could also place your hand <u>near</u> each surface of the cube (but not touching, it'll be super hot). You'll be able to feel which surface is giving off <u>more infrared radiation</u>.

Investigating IR Absorption

Have you ever noticed that wearing <u>black clothes</u> on a <u>hot day</u> makes you feel really warm?
Turns out there's some <u>science</u> behind it...

You Can Investigate **Absorption** with the **Melting Wax Trick**

The amount of infrared radiation <u>absorbed</u> by different materials also depends on the <u>surface</u>.
You can do an experiment to show this.

1) You'll need a <u>Bunsen burner</u>, <u>candle wax</u>, <u>metal plates</u> and <u>metal balls</u>.

2) The metal plates should be identical except their <u>back surface</u>, e.g. one plate will have a <u>black back</u>, and the other will have a <u>white back</u>.

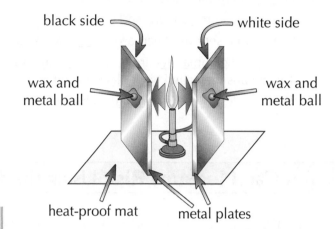

black side — white side
wax and metal ball — wax and metal ball
heat-proof mat — metal plates

3) Place the Bunsen burner on a <u>heat-proof mat</u>.

4) Stick a <u>metal ball</u> to each <u>identical side</u> of the metal plates with hot <u>candle wax</u>.

5) Leave the candle wax to <u>cool</u>. The wax will harden and hold the ball in place.

6) Then face the <u>back</u> of these plates towards the <u>flame</u>. They should both be the <u>same distance</u> away from the flame.

7) Record which ball <u>falls first</u>.

Explaining the **Results**

1) The plates absorb <u>infrared radiation</u> given out by the <u>Bunsen burner</u>.
2) <u>Energy is transferred</u> to the <u>thermal energy stores</u> of the candle wax.
3) The candle wax starts to <u>melt</u>, causing the <u>balls to fall</u>.
4) The <u>ball</u> will fall <u>quicker</u> from the plate that is <u>better</u> at absorbing <u>infrared radiation</u>.
5) You should find that the ball on the plate with the <u>black back</u> falls first.
6) This means the black surface was <u>better</u> at <u>absorbing infrared radiation</u> than the white surface.

Make sure you work safely during this practical...

You need to be <u>really careful</u> when handling the <u>hot objects</u> in this practical — make sure you use <u>protective gloves</u>. You should also <u>turn off</u> the Bunsen burner when it's not in use.

Dangers of Electromagnetic Waves

Okay, so you know how <u>useful</u> electromagnetic radiation can be — well, it can also be pretty <u>dangerous</u>.

Some **EM Radiation** Can be **Harmful** to **People**

1) When EM radiation enters <u>living tissue</u> — like <u>you</u> — it can be <u>dangerous</u>.
2) <u>High frequency</u> waves like <u>UV</u>, <u>X-rays</u> and <u>gamma rays</u> can all cause <u>lots of damage</u>.
3) <u>UV radiation</u> damages surface cells.
4) This can lead to <u>sunburn</u> and can cause <u>skin</u> to <u>age faster</u> than it should.
5) Some more serious effects are <u>blindness</u> and a <u>higher risk of skin cancer</u>.
6) <u>X-rays</u> and <u>gamma rays</u> are types of <u>ionising radiation</u>.
   This means they can <u>knock electrons off atoms</u>, p.75.
7) This can <u>destroy</u> cells or <u>mutate</u> (change) genes. This can cause <u>cancer</u>.

You Can **Measure Risk** Using the **Radiation Dose** in **Sieverts**

1) UV radiation, X-rays and gamma rays can all be
   <u>useful</u> as well as <u>harmful</u> (see page 119).
2) <u>Radiation dose</u> (measured in <u>sieverts</u>) is a measure
   of the <u>risk</u> of harm from the body being exposed to radiation.
3) The risk depends on the <u>total amount of radiation</u> absorbed
   <u>and</u> how <u>harmful</u> the <u>type</u> of radiation is.
4) A sievert is pretty big, so <u>millisieverts</u> (mSv) are often used.
   <u>1000 mSv = 1 Sv</u>.

Risk can be **Different** for **Different Parts** of the **Body**

1) A CT scan uses <u>X-rays</u> to create a detailed
   picture of inside a patient's body.
2) The table shows the <u>radiation dose</u> received
   by two <u>different parts</u> of a patient's body
   when having CT scans.

	Radiation dose (mSv)
Head	2.0
Chest	8.0

3) You can see that the radiation dose from a <u>chest scan</u> is <u>4 times larger</u>
   than from a <u>head scan</u> — (2.0 mSv × 4 = 8.0 mSv).
4) Remember, radiation dose measures the <u>risk</u> of harm.
5) This means that if a patient has a CT scan on their <u>chest</u>, they are <u>four times more
   likely</u> to be harmed than if they have a <u>head</u> scan.

The risks and benefits must be weighed up...

<u>Ionising radiation</u> can be <u>dangerous</u>, but the risk can be worth taking. <u>X-ray machines</u> used to be installed in shoe shops for use in <u>shoe fittings</u>. They were removed when people realised X-rays were harmful and the <u>risks far outweighed</u> the <u>benefits</u> of using X-rays rather than tape measures...

Warm-Up & Exam Questions

There are lots of electromagnetic waves — you never know which ones might come up in the exams so make sure you know about all of them. See how much you can remember by trying these questions.

Warm-Up Questions

1) Which type of EM wave has the highest frequency?
2) How many types of EM wave are there?
3) How are gamma rays created?
4) Give one use of infrared radiation.
5) Describe two effects that ultraviolet exposure has on the skin.

Exam Questions

1   Optical fibres have many practical uses. **Grade 1-3**

Which type of electromagnetic wave is typically transmitted in optical fibres?

☐ radio waves   ☐ microwaves

☐ visible light   ☐ X-rays

[1 mark]

2   **Figure 1** shows an image of the bones in a patient's foot. **Grade 1-3**

Figure 1

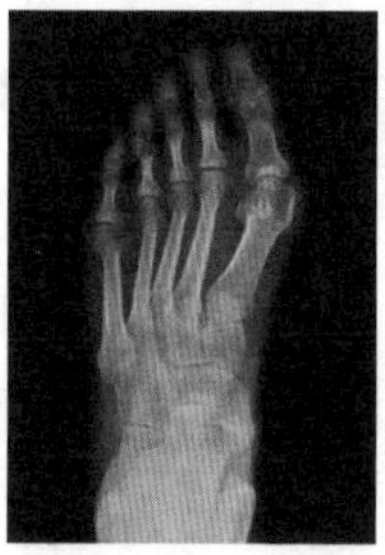

2.1   Which type of EM radiation could have been used to produce this image?

☐ radio waves   ☐ visible light

☐ microwaves   ☐ X-rays

[1 mark]

2.2   Give **one** risk to the patient from being exposed to this type of radiation.

[1 mark]

3   Some satellite signals are microwaves. **Grade 4-5**

3.1   Which of the following is high-frequency microwave radiation closest in frequency to?

☐ high-frequency ultraviolet   ☐ low-frequency visible light

☐ high-frequency radio waves   ☐ low-frequency infrared

[1 mark]

3.2   Do microwave signals travel faster in a vacuum than radio signals?
Explain your answer.

[1 mark]

Exam Questions

4   A student uses four identical beakers to investigate the infrared radiation emitted by different surfaces.

He wraps a piece of card around each beaker. Each piece of card has a different surface.

The student fills the beakers with boiling water and places a thermometer next to each one, as shown in **Figure 2**. He then records the temperature increase measured by each thermometer after two minutes.

Figure 2

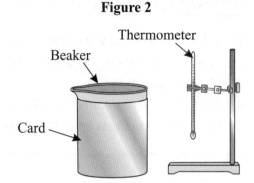

4.1   Name **one** control variable for this experiment.

[1 mark]

4.2   Name **one** safety precaution that needs to be taken in this experiment.

[1 mark]

Figure 3 shows the reading on a thermometer after it has been placed next to one of the beakers. The scale on the thermometer is in °C.

4.3   Write down the temperature shown on the thermometer. Give your answer to the nearest °C.

[1 mark]

Figure 3

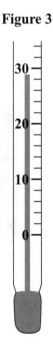

Figure 4

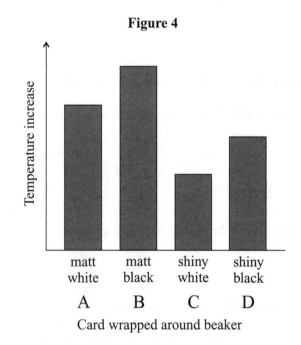

The student's results are displayed in **Figure 4**.

4.4   Some of the surfaces used in the experiment were shiny and others were matt (not shiny). Draw a conclusion from the data in **Figure 4** about how this characteristic affects infrared radiation emission.

[1 mark]

4.5   Suggest **one** way that the experiment could be made more accurate.

[1 mark]

Revision Summary for Topic 6

And that's the end of <u>Topic 6</u> — let's see how much you can remember about this topic.
- Try these questions and <u>tick off each one</u> when you <u>get it right</u>.
- When you've done <u>all the questions</u> under a heading and are <u>completely happy</u> with it, tick it off.

Wave Properties (p.109-114) ☑

1) What is the amplitude of a wave?
2) What is the wavelength of a wave?
3) What is the difference between transverse and longitudinal waves?
4) Give an example of a longitudinal wave.
5) Give the units that each quantity in the following equations should be given in:
   a) $\text{period} = \dfrac{1}{\text{frequency}}$
   b) $v = f\lambda$
6) Describe an experiment you could do to measure the speed of waves on a string.
7) Sketch a ray diagram showing the refraction of a light ray between two materials.

Uses and Dangers of Electromagnetic Waves (p.116-121) ☑

8) True or false? All electromagnetic waves are transverse.
9) Give an example of electromagnetic waves transferring energy from a source to an absorber.
10) True or false? Gamma rays have the longest wavelength of EM waves.
11) Give a common use of radio waves.
12) Which type of electromagnetic wave is used in suntanning?
13) How could you use a Leslie cube to investigate infrared emission by different surfaces?
14) True or false? The amount of infrared radiation absorbed by an object depends on the surface of the object.
15) Name two types of ionising electromagnetic radiation.
16) What does radiation dose in sieverts measure?

Magnetism

I think magnetism is an <u>attractive</u> subject, but don't get <u>repelled</u> by the exam — <u>revise</u>.

Magnets Exert **Forces** on Each Other

1) All magnets have a <u>north</u> (or <u>north seeking</u>) <u>pole</u> and a <u>south</u> (or <u>south seeking</u>) <u>pole</u>.

2) When two magnets are close, they exert a <u>non-contact force</u> on each other.

3) Two poles that are the <u>same</u> (<u>like poles</u>) <u>repel</u> each other.

Objects don't need to be touching for a non-contact force to act between them — see p.85.

4) Two <u>different</u> (<u>unlike</u>) poles <u>attract</u> each other.

5) There are also forces between magnets and <u>magnetic materials</u>. These forces are <u>always attractive</u>.

6) <u>Iron</u>, <u>steel</u>, <u>nickel</u> and <u>cobalt</u> are all magnetic materials.

Magnets Produce **Magnetic Fields**

1) The area <u>around a magnet</u> where it can exert a <u>force</u> is its <u>magnetic field</u>.

2) Magnetic fields can be shown with <u>magnetic field lines</u>.

3) The lines go from <u>north to south</u>. They show <u>which way</u> the force would push a <u>north pole</u> at that point.

4) Lines <u>closer together</u> mean a <u>stronger</u> magnetic field.

5) The <u>closer</u> to a magnet you are, the <u>stronger</u> the field is.

6) The magnetic field is <u>strongest</u> at the <u>poles</u>.

7) This means the magnetic <u>force</u> is strongest here too.

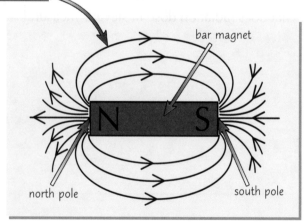

Remember magnetic field lines go from north to south...

You can see the shape of a <u>magnetic field</u> using <u>iron filings</u>. They give you a pretty pattern but they don't show you the <u>direction</u> of the <u>magnetic field</u>. That's where compasses really shine — there's more on using compasses to investigate magnetic fields on the next page.

Magnetism

Compasses aren't just useful when you're lost up a hill. They're also great tools to use to plot a magnetic field.

A **Compass** Shows the **Direction** of a Magnetic Field

1) The needle of a compass is a tiny bar magnet. It points in the direction of any magnetic field that it's in.

2) So you can use a compass to plot magnetic field patterns:

- Draw around a magnet on a piece of paper.
- Put a compass by the magnet.
- Mark the direction the compass needle points in by drawing a dot at each end of the needle.
- Move the compass so that the tail end of the needle is where the tip of the needle was before.
- Repeat this lots of times. Join up all the marks. You will end up with a drawing of one field line.

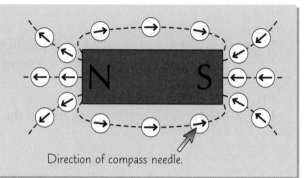

Direction of compass needle.

3) When they're not near a magnet, compasses always point north.

4) This is because they point in the direction of the Earth's magnetic field.

5) So the inside (core) of the Earth must be magnetic.

Magnets Can be **Permanent** or **Induced**

1) Permanent magnets create their own magnetic field.

2) An induced magnet turns into a magnet when it's put into another magnetic field.

3) When you take away the magnetic field, induced magnets quickly stop being magnets. A fancy way to say this is to say that they lose their magnetism (or most of it).

4) Permanent magnets and induced magnets always attract each other.

Electromagnetism

A magnetic field is also found around a wire that has a current passing through it.

A Current Creates a Magnetic Field

1) A current flowing through a wire creates a magnetic field.

2) You can see this by placing a compass near to the wire. The compass will move to point in the direction of the field.

3) You can use this to draw the field, just like on the previous page.

4) The field is made up of circles around the wire (see below).

5) You can also use the right-hand thumb rule to quickly work out which way the field goes:

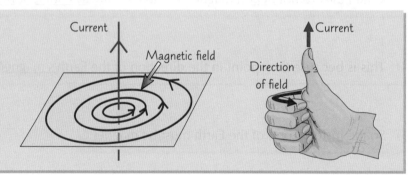

The Right-Hand Thumb Rule
- Point your right thumb in the direction of current.
- Curl your fingers.
- The direction of your fingers is the direction of the field.

6) Reversing (swapping) the direction of the current reverses the direction of the magnetic field.

7) The closer to the wire you are, the stronger the magnetic field gets.

8) And the larger the current through the wire is, the stronger the field is.

Just point your thumb in the direction of the current...

...and your fingers show the direction of the field. Remember, it's always your right thumb, not your left.

Solenoids

Electric currents can create magnetic fields (see previous page). We can use this effect to make magnets that can be switched on and off — these are electromagnets (which are made using solenoids).

A **Solenoid** is a Coil of Wire

1) If you wrap a wire into a coil it's called a solenoid.

2) The magnetic field inside a solenoid is strong and uniform.

3) Uniform means the field has the same strength and direction everywhere.

4) The magnetic field outside a coil is just like the one around a bar magnet.

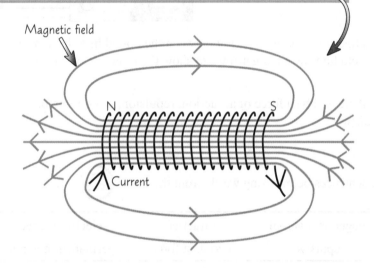

5) Wrapping a wire into a solenoid increases the strength of the magnetic field produced by the current in the wire.

- This is because the field lines around each loop of wire line up with each other.
- So lots of field lines end up close to each other and pointing in the same direction.
- The closer together field lines are, the stronger the field is.

6) You can increase the field strength even more by putting a block of iron in the coil.

7) A solenoid with an iron core is called an electromagnet.

Fields around solenoids and bar magnets are the same shape...

Electromagnets pop up in lots of different places — they're used in electric bells, car ignition circuits and some security doors. Electromagnets aren't all the same strength though — how strong they are depends on stuff like the number of turns of wire there are and the size of the current going through the wire.

Warm-Up & Exam Questions

Time to test your knowledge — as usual, make sure you're switched on by doing the warm-up questions, then dive into the exam questions. Don't forget to go back and check up on any bits you can't do.

Warm-Up Questions

1) Draw a diagram to show the magnetic field around a single bar magnet. Indicate its direction with arrows.

2) When using the right-hand thumb rule, what does the direction of your fingers represent?

3) How can you form a solenoid from a current-carrying wire?

Exam Questions

1 A student arranges two magnets as shown in **Figure 1**.

Figure 1

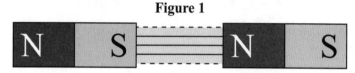

1.1 Magnetic field lines in the shaded region between the dotted lines have been drawn on **Figure 1**. Complete the field lines by adding arrows to show the direction of the field.

[1 mark]

1.2 State whether there will be a force of attraction, repulsion, or no force between the two magnets. Explain your answer.

[2 marks]

2 Complete the sentences below using words from the box.

magnetic material	attractive	electromagnet
repulsive	a contact force	permanent magnet

Cobalt is an example of a .... The force between

a piece of cobalt and a bar magnet is always ....

[2 marks]

3 A student is investigating magnetic fields. She passes a wire through a horizontal piece of card and connects it in an electrical circuit, as shown in **Figure 2**.

Figure 2

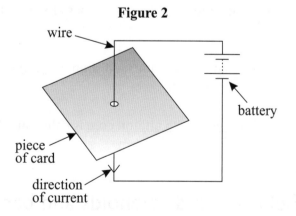

3.1 The student uses a compass to plot the magnetic field lines on the piece of card. Describe the shape and direction of the magnetic field the student will plot.

[2 marks]

3.2 The student forms the wire into a coil. Explain why this leads to an increase in the magnetic field strength.

[2 marks]

Revision Summary for Topic 7

That wraps up <u>Topic 7</u> — time to put yourself to the test and find out <u>how much you really know</u>.

- Try these questions and <u>tick off each one</u> when you <u>get it right</u>.
- When you've done <u>all the questions</u> under a heading and are <u>completely happy</u> with it, tick it off.

Magnets (p.126-127) ☐

1) True or false? The force between a north pole and a south pole is attractive. ☑
2) Give three magnetic materials. ☑
3) In what direction do magnetic field lines point? ☑
4) True or False? The closer together the magnetic field lines are, the stronger the magnetic field. ☑
5) Where on a bar magnet is the magnetic force strongest? ☑
6) How can you draw the magnetic field pattern of a bar magnet using a compass? ☑
7) Describe the behaviour of a compass that is far away from any magnets. ☑
8) What is meant by an 'induced magnet'? ☑

Electromagnetism (p.128-129) ☑

9) Explain how to use the right-hand thumb rule to find the direction of a magnetic field around a wire. ☑
10) How can the direction of the magnetic field around a current-carrying wire be reversed? ☑
11) True or false? The magnetic field around a current-carrying wire gets weaker closer to the wire. ☑
12) Sketch the shape of the magnetic field around a solenoid. ☑
13) Describe the magnetic field inside a solenoid. ☑
14) What can be added to a solenoid to make it into an electromagnet? ☑

Measuring Lengths and Angles

Get your lab coat on, it's time to find out about the skills you'll need in <u>experiments</u>.
First things first — make sure you're using <u>appropriate equipment</u> and know <u>how to use it</u> correctly.

Measure **Most Lengths** with a **Ruler**

1) Make sure you <u>choose</u> the <u>right ruler</u> to measure length:

   - In most cases a <u>centimetre ruler</u> can be used.
   - <u>Metre rulers</u> are handy for <u>large</u> distances.
   - <u>Micrometers</u> are used for measuring <u>tiny</u> things (e.g. the <u>diameter of a wire</u>).

2) The ruler should always be <u>alongside</u> what you want to measure.

3) It may be <u>tricky</u> to measure just <u>one</u> of something (e.g. water ripples, p.113). Instead, you can measure the length of <u>ten</u> of them together. Then <u>divide by ten</u> to find the <u>length of one</u>.

4) You might need to take <u>lots of measurements</u> of the <u>same</u> object (e.g. a spring). If so, make sure you always measure from the <u>same point</u> on the object.

5) Drawing or sticking a <u>marker</u> onto the object can be useful. It gives you something to <u>line up</u> your ruler against.

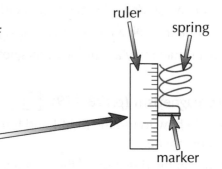

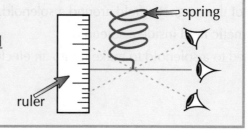

Make sure the ruler and the object are always at <u>eye level</u> when you take a reading.

Use a **Protractor** to Find **Angles**

1) Place the <u>middle</u> of the protractor on the <u>pointy bit</u> of the angle.

2) <u>Line up</u> the <u>base line</u> of the protractor with one line of the angle.

3) Use the <u>scale</u> on the protractor to measure the angle of the other line.

4) Use a <u>sharp pencil</u> to draw lines at an angle (e.g. in ray diagrams). This helps to <u>reduce errors</u> when measuring the angles.

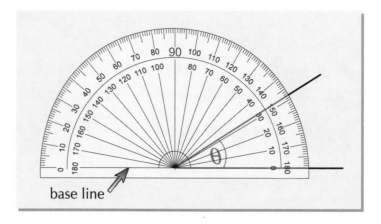

Measuring Volumes

Did you order some more measuring? Well, even if you didn't, here's some stuff about <u>measuring volumes</u>.

Different Ways to Measure **Liquids**

There are a few methods you might use to <u>transfer</u> a <u>volume of liquid</u>:

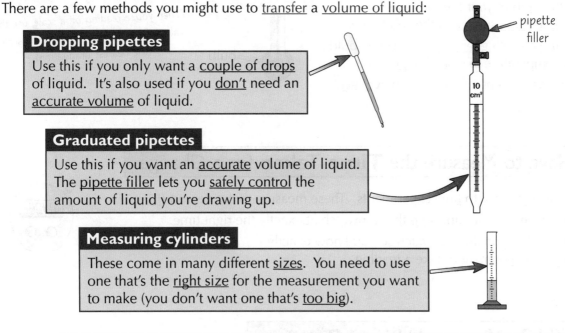

pipette filler

Dropping pipettes

Use this if you only want a <u>couple of drops</u> of liquid. It's also used if you <u>don't</u> need an <u>accurate volume</u> of liquid.

Graduated pipettes

Use this if you want an <u>accurate</u> volume of liquid. The <u>pipette filler</u> lets you <u>safely control</u> the amount of liquid you're drawing up.

Measuring cylinders

These come in many different <u>sizes</u>. You need to use one that's the <u>right size</u> for the measurement you want to make (you don't want one that's <u>too big</u>).

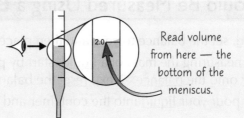

To measure the volume of a liquid, read the volume from the <u>bottom</u> of the <u>meniscus</u> (the curved upper surface of the liquid) when it's at <u>eye level</u>.

Read volume from here — the bottom of the meniscus.

Eureka Cans Measure the **Volumes** of **Solids**

1) A <u>eureka can</u> is a <u>beaker with a spout</u>.

2) It's used with a <u>measuring cylinder</u> to find the <u>volume</u> of an <u>irregularly shaped solid object</u>.

3) How to use a eureka can to find an object's <u>volume</u> is explained on page 66.

4) Here are a few extra <u>tips</u> to increase the <u>accuracy</u> of your results:

- Fill the can with water so the water level is <u>above the spout</u>.

- Then let the water <u>drain</u> from the spout, leaving the water level <u>just below</u> the start of the spout. (This means <u>all</u> the water moved by an object goes into the measuring cylinder.)

- After adding the object, wait until the spout has <u>stopped dripping</u> before measuring the volume.

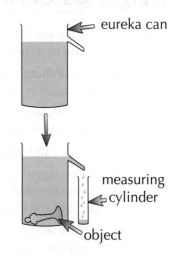

eureka can

measuring cylinder

object

You might have to bend down a little...

Whether you're reading off a ruler, a pipette or a measuring cylinder, make sure you take all readings at <u>eye level</u>. And, if you're taking a reading for a volume, make sure you measure from the bottom of the <u>meniscus</u> (that's from the dip in the curved surface at the top of the liquid).

More on Measuring

Temperature, mass, time, acceleration — you can bet your boots that these quantities need measuring too.

Measure **Temperature** Using a **Thermometer**

1) Make sure the <u>bulb</u> of your thermometer is <u>completely under the surface</u> of the substance.

2) If you're taking a <u>starting temperature</u>, you should wait for the temperature to <u>stop changing</u>.

3) Read your measurement off the <u>scale</u> at <u>eye level</u>.

bulb

When you're reading off a scale, use the value of the nearest mark on the scale (the nearest graduation).

You May Have to Measure the **Time Taken** for a Change

1) You can use a <u>stopwatch</u> to <u>time</u> experiments. These measure to the nearest <u>0.1 s</u>.

2) Always make sure you <u>start</u> and <u>stop</u> the stopwatch at exactly the right time.

3) You can set an <u>alarm</u> on the stopwatch so you know exactly when to stop an experiment or take a reading.

Mass Should Be Measured Using a **Balance**

1) For a <u>solid</u>, set the balance to <u>zero</u> and then place your object onto the scale and read off the mass.

2) If you're measuring the mass of a <u>liquid</u>, start by putting an empty <u>container</u> onto the <u>balance</u>. Next, <u>reset</u> the balance to zero.

3) Then just pour your <u>liquid</u> into the container and record the mass displayed. Easy peasy.

Light Gates Measure **Time, Speed** and **Acceleration**

1) A <u>light gate</u> sends a <u>beam</u> of light from <u>one side</u> of the gate to a <u>detector</u> on the <u>other side</u>.

2) When something passes through the gate, the light beam is <u>interrupted</u>.

3) The gate measures <u>when</u> the beam was interrupted and <u>how long</u> it was interrupted for.

4) Light gates can be connected to a <u>computer</u>.

5) To find the <u>speed</u> of an object, type the <u>length</u> of the object into the computer. The computer will <u>calculate</u> the speed of the object as it passes through the beam.

6) To measure <u>acceleration</u>, use an object that interrupts the signal <u>twice</u>, e.g. a piece of card with a gap cut into the middle.

7) The light gate measures the speed for <u>each section</u> of the object. It uses this to calculate the object's <u>acceleration</u>. This can then be read from the <u>computer screen</u>.

8) Light gates can be used instead of a <u>stopwatch</u>. This will <u>reduce the errors</u> in your experiment.

light gate
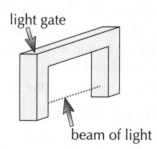
beam of light

Have a look at page 102 for an example of a light gate being used.

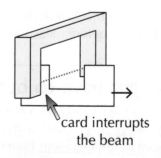
card interrupts the beam

Working With Electronics

Electrical devices are used in a bunch of experiments, so make sure you know how to use them.

You Have to Interpret **Circuit Diagrams**

Before you get cracking on an experiment involving any kind of electrical devices, you have to plan and build your circuit using a circuit diagram. Make sure you know all of the circuit symbols on page 41 so you're not stumped before you've even started.

You Can Measure **Potential Difference** and **Current**

Voltmeters Measure Potential Difference

1) Connect the voltmeter in parallel (p.52) across the component you want to test.

2) The wires that come with a voltmeter are usually red (positive) and black (negative). These go into the red and black coloured ports on the voltmeter.

3) Then read the potential difference from the scale (or from the screen if the voltmeter is digital).

Ammeters Measure Current

1) Connect the ammeter in series (p.50) with the component you want to test.

2) Ammeters usually have red and black ports to show you where to connect your wires.

3) Read off the current shown on the scale (or screen).

Turn your circuit off between readings to prevent wires overheating and affecting your results (p.43).

Multimeters Measure Both

1) Multimeters measure a range of things — usually potential difference, current and resistance.

2) To find potential difference, plug the red wire into the port that has a '**V**' (for volts).

3) To find the current, use the port labelled '**A**' (for amps).

4) The dial on the multimeter should then be turned to the relevant section — for example, to measure the current in amps, turn the dial to '**A**'.

5) The screen will display the value you're measuring.

Don't get your wires in a tangle when you're using circuits...

When you're dealing with voltmeters, ammeters and multimeters, you need to make sure that you wire them into your circuit correctly, otherwise you could mess up your readings. Just remember, the red wires should go into the red ports and the black wires should go into the black ports.

Safety and Experiments

There's <u>danger</u> all around, particularly in science experiments. But don't let this put you off. Just be aware of the <u>hazards</u> and take <u>sensible precautions</u>. Read on to find out more...

To Make Sure You're **Working Safely** in the **Lab** You Need to...

1) Be aware of <u>general safety</u> in the lab. E.g. don't touch any <u>hot equipment</u>.

2) Follow any <u>instructions</u> that your teacher gives you <u>carefully</u>.

3) Use <u>clamp stands</u> to stop masses and equipment falling.

4) Make sure <u>masses</u> are <u>not too heavy</u> (so they <u>don't break</u> the equipment they're used with).

5) Use <u>pulleys</u> that are <u>not too long</u> (so hanging masses <u>don't hit the floor</u> during the experiment).

6) Let hot materials <u>cool</u> before moving them. Or wear <u>insulated gloves</u> while handling them.

7) If you're using an <u>immersion heater</u>, you should always let it <u>dry out</u> in air. This is just in case any liquid has <u>leaked</u> inside the heater.

8) If you're using a <u>laser</u>, there are a few safety rules you must follow:
   - Always wear <u>laser safety goggles</u>.
   - Never <u>look directly into</u> the laser or shine it <u>towards another person</u>.
   - Make sure you turn the laser <u>off</u> if it's not needed to avoid any accidents.

9) When working with electronics, make sure you use a <u>low voltage</u> and <u>current</u>. This prevents the wires <u>overheating</u>. It also stops <u>damage to components</u>.

BEWARE — hazardous physics experiments about...

Before you carry out an experiment, it's important to consider all of the <u>hazards</u>. Hazards can be anything from <u>lasers</u> to <u>electrical currents</u>, or weights to heating equipment. Whatever the hazards, make sure you know all the <u>safety precautions</u> you should follow to keep yourself <u>safe</u>.

GCSE Combined Science

Physics Paper 1

Foundation Tier

Centre name				
Centre number				
Candidate number				

In addition to this paper you should have:
- A ruler.
- A calculator.
- The Physics Equation sheet (on the inside back cover).

Time allowed:
- 1 hour 15 minutes

Surname	
Other names	
Candidate signature	

Instructions to candidates
- Write your name and other details in the spaces provided above.
- Answer **all** questions in the spaces provided.
- Do all rough work on the paper.
- Cross out any work you do not want to be marked.

Information for candidates
- The marks available are given in brackets at the end of each question.
- There are 70 marks available for this paper.
- You are allowed to use a calculator.
- You should use good English and present your answers in a clear and organised way.
- For Questions 5.1 and 7.7 ensure that your answers have a clear and logical structure, include the right scientific terms, are spelt correctly and include detailed, relevant information.

Advice to candidates
- In calculations, show clearly how you worked out your answers.

For examiner's use

Q	Attempt Nº 1	2	3	Q	Attempt Nº 1	2	3
1				5			
2				6			
3				7			
4							
Total							

1 A representation of the particles of a substance is shown in **Figure 1**.

Figure 1

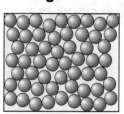

1.1 Name the state of matter of the substance shown in **Figure 1**.

....

[1 mark]

1.2 The substance in **Figure 1** is heated. This increases the particle's internal energy.
Which of the particle's energy stores is energy transferred to?
Tick **two** boxes.

☐ potential energy

☐ nuclear energy

☐ chemical energy

☐ kinetic energy

☐ magnetic energy

[2 marks]

Figure 2 shows a sketch of the heating curve for a 1.0 kg sample of the substance.

Figure 2

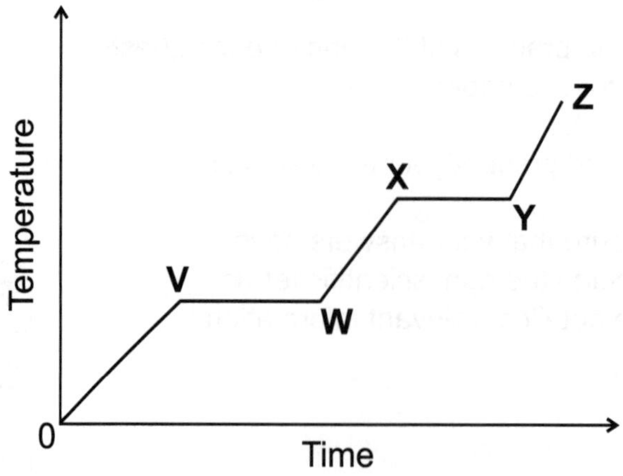

1.3 Identify the state of matter of the substance at point **Z**.

....

[1 mark]

1.4 At which point in **Figure 2** has the substance reached its boiling point?
Tick **one** box.

☐ V
☐ W
☐ X
☐ Z

[1 mark]

Between points **V** and **W**, 334 000 J is supplied to the 1.0 kg sample of the substance.

1.5 Which of the following statements is true?
Tick **one** box.

☐ The specific latent heat of fusion of the substance is 334 000 J/kg.

☐ The specific heat capacity of the substance is 334 000 J/kg.

☐ The specific latent heat of vaporisation of the substance is 334 000 J/kg.

[1 mark]

1.6 Calculate the minimum amount of energy that would need to be
transferred from a 5.00 kg sample of the substance to freeze it.
Use the correct equation from the Physics Equation Sheet on the inside cover.

....

....

Energy = ... J
[2 marks]

Turn over for the next question

2   A student wants to find the density of an ornament.
Figure 3 shows the ornament.

Figure 3

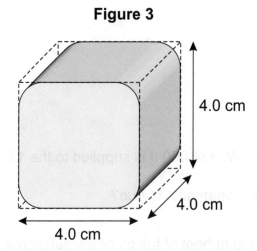

2.1   Estimate the volume of the ornament by calculating the volume of the cube shown in
Figure 3. Give your answer in cm³.

....

....

Volume = ... cm³
[2 marks]

The student decides to measure the volume accurately using a eureka can and
measuring cylinder.

He fills a eureka can with water so that it is full up to the base of the spout. When
he places the ornament in the eureka can, water will pour into a measuring cylinder.
Figure 4 shows the eureka can before and after the ornament has been added.

Figure 4

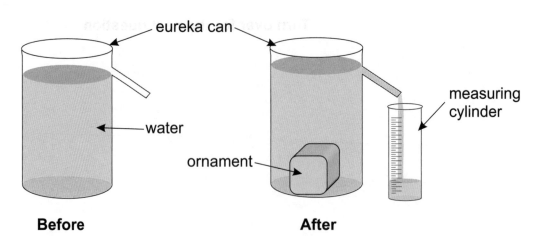

Figure 5 shows two measuring cylinders, **A** and **B**, that the student could use to collect water from the eureka can.

Figure 5

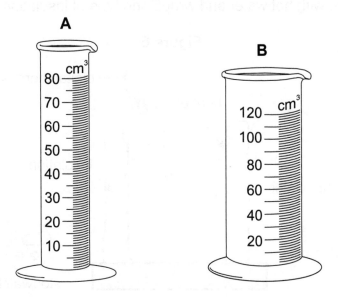

2.2 State and explain which cylinder the student should use for his experiment.

....

....
[1 mark]

2.3 The student finds that the volume of the ornament is 0.000058 m³.
He measures the mass of the ornament to be 0.435 kg.

Use the following equation to calculate the density of the ornament.

$$density = \frac{mass}{volume}$$

....

....

Density = ... kg/m³
[2 marks]

Turn over for the next question

Turn over ▶

3   A home owner wants to wrap insulation around her hot water tank to reduce unwanted energy transfers. She needs to choose between three different types of insulation.

She does an experiment to test which type of insulation would be the best to use. She fills a beaker with hot water and wraps one type of insulation around it, as shown in **Figure 6**.

Figure 6

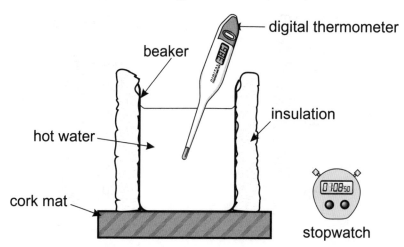

She measures the temperature decrease of the water after 5 minutes. She repeats this experiment with each type of insulation.

3.1   State the independent variable in this investigation.

....
[1 mark]

3.2   State **two** control variables in this investigation.

1. ....

2. ....
[2 marks]

The home owner repeats her experiment three times for each type of insulation. Her results for one type of insulation are shown in **Table 1**.

Table 1

Temperature decrease (°C)			
1	**2**	**3**	**Mean**
21.9	22.2	20.1	

3.3   Use the data in **Table 1** to calculate the mean temperature decrease for the insulation.

....

....

Mean temperature decrease = ... °C
[2 marks]

The home owner finds the temperature decrease for each type of insulation is roughly the same. She realises this is due to the way she set up the apparatus shown in **Figure 6**.

3.4 Using **Figure 6**, identify the mistake the home owner has made.
Explain why this mistake would have caused the temperature decreases recorded to be roughly the same for each type of insulation.

....

....

....

[3 marks]

3.5 Which of the following best describes how the homeowner should insulate her tank to minimise unwanted energy transfers to the surroundings?
Tick **one** box.

☐ With a thick layer of material that has a low thermal conductivity.

☐ With a thin layer of material that has a low thermal conductivity.

☐ With a thick layer of material that has a high thermal conductivity.

☐ With a thin layer of material that has a high thermal conductivity.

[1 mark]

The home owner also wishes to use more energy from renewable energy resources to reduce her energy bills. She wants to generate electricity either using the wind or directly from the Sun.

3.6 Give **one** other example of a renewable energy resource.

....

[1 mark]

Table 2 gives some data about the costs and savings of generating electricity using solar panels or a wind turbine.

Table 2

	Installation cost	Average annual energy bill saving
Solar panels	£6000	£375
Wind turbine	£10 000	£500

3.7 The home owner expects to move house in 10 years time.
Evaluate whether she would save money by having solar panels installed.
Use data from **Table 2** in your answer.

....

....

....

[2 marks]

Turn over for the next question

Turn over ▶

4   A student is investigating the two electrical circuits shown in **Figure 7**.
     The resistors and batteries used in each circuit are identical.

Figure 7

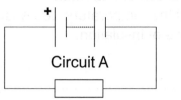

Circuit A

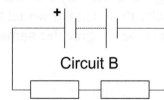

Circuit B

4.1   Which statement correctly describes the total resistance of circuit B?
      Tick **one** box.

☐ It is half as large as the resistance of circuit A.

☐ It is the same as the resistance of circuit A.

☐ It is twice as large as the resistance of circuit A.

[1 mark]

4.2   Compare the current in circuits A and B. Explain your answer.

....

....
[2 marks]

4.3   The total potential difference across the resistor in circuit A is 12 V.
      Which statement about the potential difference across the resistors in circuit B is true?
      Tick **one** box.

☐ The potential difference across each resistor is 6 V.

☐ The potential difference across each resistor is 12 V.

☐ The potential difference across each resistor is 24 V.

[1 mark]

4.4   The resistor in circuit A has a resistance of 4.0 Ω. The current through it is 3.0 A.
      Use the following equation to calculate the power dissipated by the resistor in circuit A.

power = (current)^2 × resistance

Choose the correct unit from the box. | **joules   watts   newtons per metre** |

....

....

Power = ...

Unit = ...
[3 marks]

The student considers adding one of the components in **Figure 8** to circuit A.

Figure 8

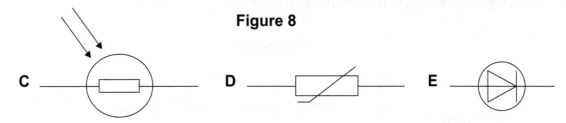

4.5 What happens to the resistance of component **C** as the intensity of light that falls on it increases?
Tick **one** box.

☐ The resistance increases.

☐ The resistance remains constant.

☐ The resistance decreases.

[1 mark]

4.6 Suggest **one** application for component **D**.

....

....

[1 mark]

4.7 On the axes in **Figure 9**, sketch the *I-V* characteristic of component **E**.

Figure 9

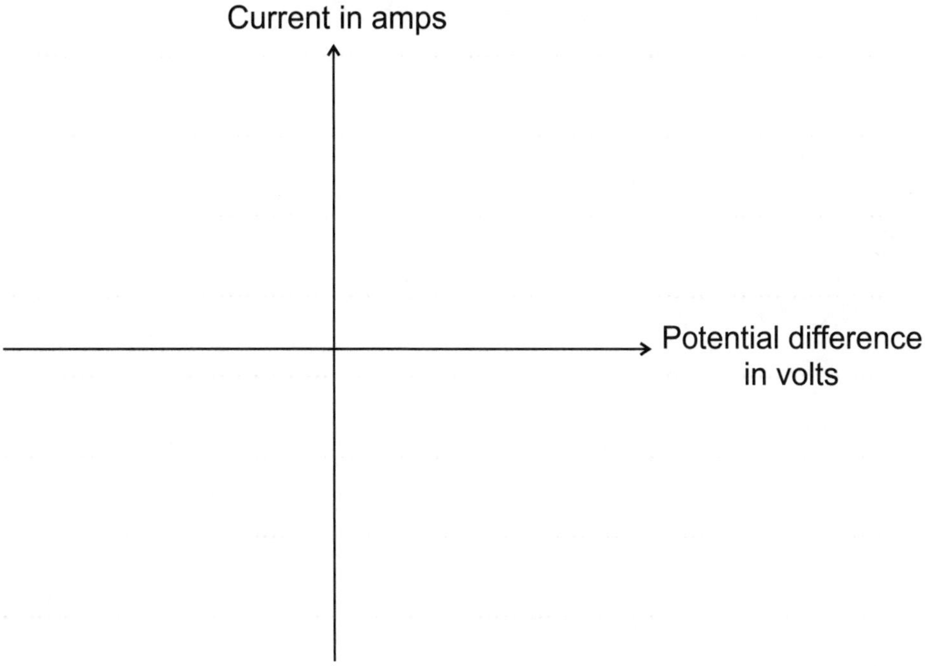

Current in amps

Potential difference in volts

[2 marks]

Turn over for the next question

Turn over ▶

5 A student uses the circuit shown in **Figure 10** to investigate how the length of the test wire affects its resistance.

Figure 10

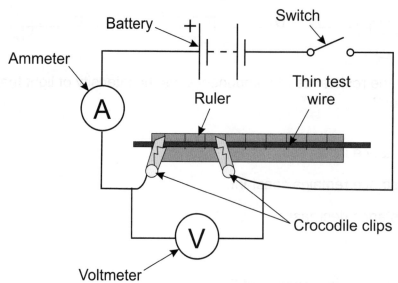

5.1 Describe a method the student could use for her investigation.
Include steps to make sure the results are as accurate as possible.

....

....

....

....

....

....

....

....

....

....

....

....

[6 marks]

The student records her results in **Table 3**.

Table 3

Length / cm	Resistance / mΩ
5	6.7
10	13.4
15	20.1
20	26.8
25	33.5

5.2 **Figure 11** shows an incomplete graph of the student's results. Using **Table 3**, complete **Figure 11** by plotting the remaining points. Draw a line of best fit.

Figure 11

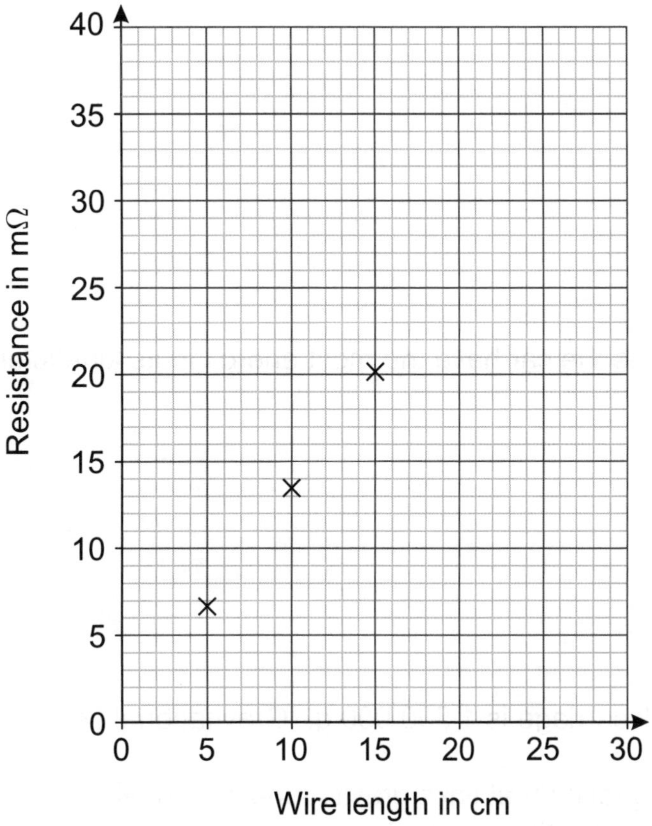

Wire length in cm

[2 marks]

5.3 Predict the resistance of a test wire with a length of 30 cm.

Resistance = ... mΩ

[1 mark]

5.4 Give **one** conclusion that can be made from **Figure 11**.

....

....

[1 mark]

Turn over for the next question

Turn over ▶

6   At the start of a roller coaster ride a carriage is raised by a chain lift through a vertical height of 40 m to point **W**, as shown in **Figure 12**. It is stopped at point **W** and then released to follow the track through points **X**, **Y** and **Z**.

Figure 12

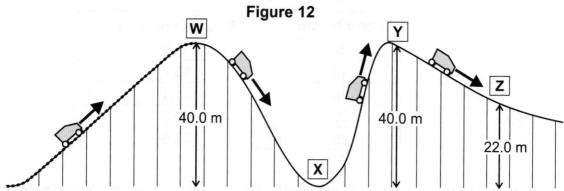

6.1   At which two points does the carriage have the same amount of energy in its gravitational potential energy store? Tick **one** box.

☐   **X** and **Z**.

☐   **W** and **Y**

☐   **Y** and **Z**

☐   **W** and **Z**

[1 mark]

6.2   At which point does the car have the most energy in its kinetic energy store?
Tick **one** box.

☐   **W**

☐   **X**

☐   **Z**

[1 mark]

The mass of a full carriage is 1 500 000 g. Gravitational field strength = 9.8 N/kg.

6.3   Write down the equation that links gravitational potential energy, mass, height and gravitational field strength.

....

[1 mark]

6.4   Calculate the energy transferred to the gravitational potential energy store of a full carriage as it is raised by the chain lift to point **W**.

....

....

Energy transferred = ... J

[2 marks]

A different type of roller coaster uses a spring system to launch a carriage forward.
A compressed spring extends, causing an energy transfer that launches the carriage.

6.5 State the energy store that energy is transferred from when the compressed
spring extends.

....
[1 mark]

6.6 State the equation linking efficiency, useful energy output and total energy output.

....
[1 mark]

6.7 The spring system stores 59.5 kJ of energy when it is compressed.
When a carriage is launched, 18.0 kJ of this energy is usefully
transferred to the kinetic energy store of the carriage.

Calculate the efficiency of the spring system.
Give your answer to three significant figures.

....

....

Efficiency = ...
[2 marks]

6.8 Explain why lubricating the moving parts of the carriage will increase its speed.
Include the energy store that energy is usefully transferred to in your answer.

....

....

....

....

....
[3 marks]

Turn over for the next question

Turn over ▶

7   **Table 4** gives details of some isotopes.

Table 4

Isotope	Symbol	Type of decay
Radium-226	$^{226}_{88}Ra$	alpha
Radon-222	$^{222}_{86}Rn$	alpha
Radon-224	$^{224}_{86}Rn$	beta
Bismuth-210	$^{210}_{83}Bi$	alpha, beta
Bismuth-214	$^{214}_{83}Bi$	alpha, beta
Lead-210	$^{210}_{82}Pb$	beta

7.1   Calculate the number of neutrons in a bismuth-214 nucleus.

....
[1 mark]

7.2   Explain why bismuth-210 and bismuth-214 are isotopes of each other.

....

....
[2 marks]

7.3   Using data from **Table 4**, complete the equations in **Figure 13** to show how the following isotopes decay.

Figure 13

$$^{226}_{88}Ra \longrightarrow \boxed{} + \boxed{^{4}_{2}He}$$

$$^{210}_{82}Pb \longrightarrow \boxed{} + \boxed{^{0}_{-1}e}$$

[2 marks]

Figure 14 shows the activity-time graph of a sample of polonium-210.

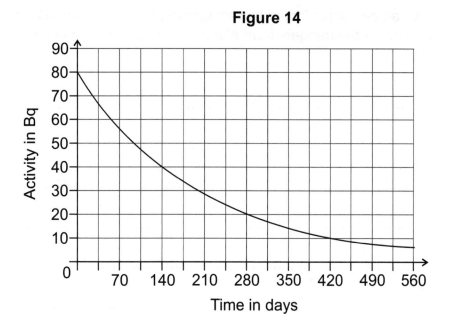

Figure 14

7.4   Using the graph in **Figure 14**, determine the time it takes for the activity of the sample to drop from 80 Bq to 10 Bq.

Time taken = ... days

[1 mark]

7.5   Determine the half-life of polonium-210.

Half-life = ... days

[1 mark]

Polonium-210 emits alpha radiation. Scientists who work with it must be particularly careful to avoid radioactive contamination.

7.6   Define the term radioactive contamination.

....

....

....

[1 mark]

Question 7 continues on the next page

Turn over ▶

Another isotope of polonium, polonium-217, emits both alpha and beta particles.

7.7 A human body can be contaminated by radioactive atoms on the inside or on the outside. Explain and compare the dangers from alpha and beta radiation in both of these situations.

....

....

....

....

....

....

....

....

....

[4 marks]

END OF QUESTIONS

Practice Exam Paper GCSE Combined Science

GCSE Combined Science

Physics Paper 2

Foundation Tier

In addition to this paper you should have:
- A ruler.
- A calculator.
- The Physics Equation sheet
  (on the inside back cover).

Centre name					
Centre number					
Candidate number					

Time allowed:
- 1 hour 15 minutes

Surname	
Other names	
Candidate signature	

Instructions to candidates
- Write your name and other details in the spaces provided above.
- Answer **all** questions in the spaces provided.
- Do all rough work on the paper.
- Cross out any work you do not want to be marked.

Information for candidates
- The marks available are given in brackets at the end of each question.
- There are 70 marks available for this paper.
- You are allowed to use a calculator.
- You should use good English and present your answers in a clear and organised way.
- For Questions 3.6 and 7.3 ensure that your answers have a clear and logical structure, include the right scientific terms, are spelt correctly and include detailed, relevant information.

Advice to candidates
- In calculations, show clearly how you worked out your answers.

For examiner's use

Q	Attempt Nº			Q	Attempt Nº		
	1	2	3		1	2	3
1				5			
2				6			
3				7			
4							
Total							

1   A student is given apparatus to investigate the relationship between the force
     on a spring and its extension. The apparatus is set up as shown in **Figure 1**.
     The hook is assumed to have zero mass.

Figure 1

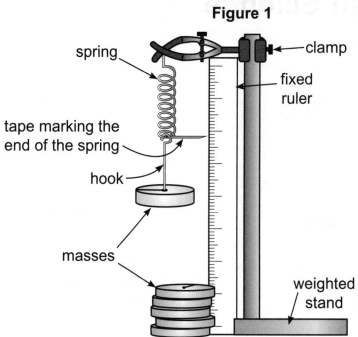

1.1   Placing one of the masses on the hook exerts a force of 1 N on the bottom
       of the spring.
       A force is exerted by the clamp on the other end of the spring.
       What is the size of the force exerted on the spring by the clamp?
       Tick **one** box.

       ☐   0.5 N

       ☐   1 N

       ☐   1.5 N

       ☐   2 N

                                                                              [1 mark]

1.2   Explain why more than one force is needed to deform a spring.

       ....

       ....
                                                                              [1 mark]

1.3   Name the type of error which may be reduced by the use of the tape marker
       at the end of the spring when taking extension measurements.
       Tick **one** box.

           ☐   zero error

           ☐   systematic error

           ☐   random error

                                                                              [1 mark]

The student used the apparatus in **Figure 1** to collect data and plot the graph shown in **Figure 2**.

Figure 2

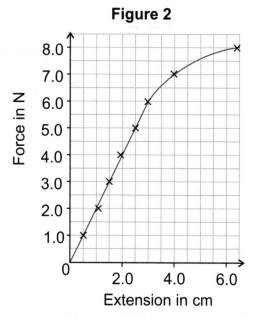

1.4   Estimate the maximum force that can be applied to the spring before the limit of proportionality is reached. Use **Figure 2** to justify your estimate.

....

....

....

[2 marks]

1.5   Use the graph to find the force needed to produce an extension of 0.015 m.

Force = ... N

[2 marks]

1.6   Use the following equation to calculate the spring constant of the spring.

Spring constant = force ÷ extension

....

....

Spring constant = ... N/m

[2 marks]

Turn over for the next question

Turn over ▶

2   A swimmer swims a length of a 20 m swimming pool.
The distance-time graph in **Figure 3** shows the swimmer's motion.

Figure 3

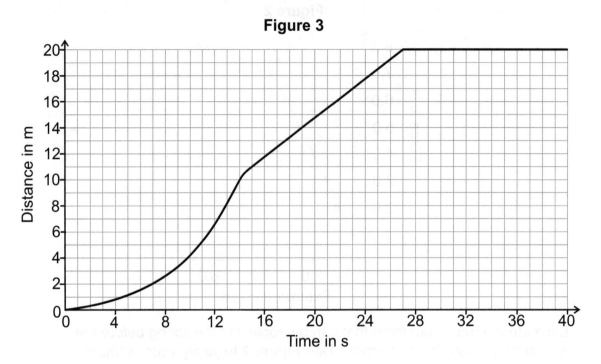

Between 15 and 27 seconds the swimmer is travelling at constant speed.

2.1   State the resultant force on the swimmer between 15 and 27 seconds.

Force = ... N
[1 mark]

2.2   Using **Figure 3**, calculate the speed of the swimmer between 15 and 27 seconds.

....

....

Speed = ... m/s
[2 marks]

2.3   Between which of the following distances was the swimmer travelling fastest?
Tick **one** box.

☐   Between 14 metres and 15 metres.

☐   Between 9 metres and 10 metres.

☐   Between 0 metres and 1 metre.

[1 mark]

A camera travels along the length of the pool to film the swimmer.
It starts from rest at the same time as the swimmer.
It travels at a constant speed and reaches the end of the pool in 23 s.

2.4 Use the following equation to calculate the speed of the camera.

$$speed = \frac{distance\ travelled}{time}$$

Give your answer to 2 significant figures.

....

....

Speed = ... m/s
[2 marks]

2.5 Draw a distance-time graph on **Figure 3** to show the motion of the camera.
[2 marks]

2.6 The swimmer swims back to their starting position.
Which of the following statements is true when they have returned
to their starting position?
Tick **one** box.

☐ The magnitude of the swimmer's displacement is 40 m.

☐ The distance the swimmer has travelled is 20 m.

☐ The magnitude of the swimmer's displacement is 0 m.

☐ The distance the swimmer has travelled is 0 m.

[1 mark]

Turn over for the next question

Turn over ▶

3   Electromagnetic waves are a type of transverse wave.
A trace of a transverse wave is displayed in **Figure 4**.

Figure 4

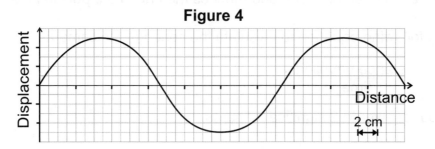

3.1   Calculate the amplitude of the wave in **Figure 4**.

....

Amplitude = ... cm

[1 mark]

3.2   What is the frequency of a wave?
Tick **one** box.

☐   The amount of energy carried by the wave

☐   How long it takes for a complete wave to be produced.

☐   The number of complete waves that pass a point each second.

☐   The average displacement of a point on a wave from the rest position.

[1 mark]

3.3   Infrared radiation is emitted by some TV remote controls. Give **one** other use of infrared.

....

[1 mark]

When infrared radiation reaches a material it can do three things: (1) be absorbed,
(2) bounce back, or (3) pass straight through it.

A student sets up the experiment shown in **Figure 5** to test whether a material absorbs
infrared. The TVs will switch on if infrared radiation from the remote control reached
them. The student believes that if the material absorbs the infrared radiation, the TVs
will remain off.

Figure 5

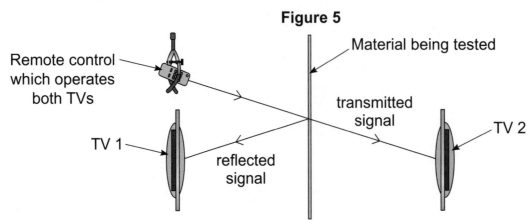

3.4 **Variable 1** and **Variable 2** are listed below. What types of variable are they?
Tick **one** box for **Variable 1** and **one** box for **Variable 2**.

	Independent	Dependent	Control
Variable 1: Distance of remote from material	☐	☐	☐
Variable 2: Type of material being tested	☐	☐	☐

[2 marks]

The student makes the hypothesis:
'Only dark-coloured materials absorb infrared signals.'
The student's results are shown in **Table 1**.

Table 1

Material	Which TVs respond?	Signal absorbed?
white paper	TV 1 and TV 2	no
black paper	neither	yes
white woollen blanket	neither	yes
black woollen blanket	neither	yes

3.5 Explain whether the student's results in **Table 1** support their hypothesis.

....

....

[1 mark]

3.6 Remote controls can use infrared waves or radio waves to send signals to devices.
Describe the similarities and differences between infrared waves and radio waves.

....

....

....

....

....

....

[4 marks]

Turn over for the next question

Turn over ▶

4   A student sets up the apparatus shown in **Figure 6** to investigate a wave on a string. The student adjusts the frequency of the signal generator until there is a clear wave on the string.

Figure 6

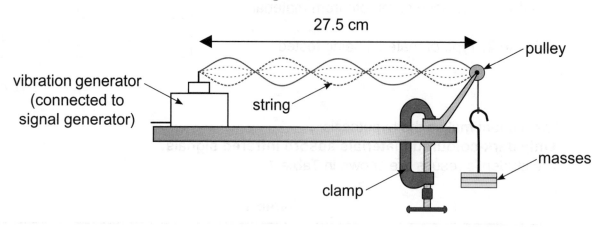

4.1   State **one** safety precaution that the student should take when doing this experiment.

....

....

[1 mark]

4.2   What is the wavelength of the wave on the string shown in **Figure 6**?
Tick **one** box.

☐   5.50 cm

☐   11.0 cm

☐   13.75 cm

☐   27.5 cm

[1 mark]

4.3   Write down the equation that links wave speed, frequency and wavelength.

....

[1 mark]

4.4   The signal generator is set to 120 Hz. Calculate the speed of the wave on the string.

....

....

Speed = ... m/s

[2 marks]

4.5 The student sets up a wave on another string and calculates its speed.
She repeats this four times with the same string. Her results are:

12.8 m/s   13.4 m/s   13.3 m/s   32.9 m/s

Identify any anomalous results in the set.
Describe how such anomalous results should be dealt with.

....

....

....

....

[3 marks]

The student decides to investigate how the diameter of the string is related to wave speed. She will use four strings made of the same material with different diameters.

4.6 The student plans to measure the diameters of the strings using a 30 cm ruler.
Explain why this equipment is unsuitable.
Suggest a more suitable piece of equipment that could be used.

....

....

....

[2 marks]

The student's results are shown in **Table 2**.

Table 2

String diameter (mm)	0.26	0.68	1.33	2.15
Wave speed (m/s)	25.8	9.86	5.04	3.12

4.7 Give **one** conclusion that can be made from the results in **Table 2**.

....

....

[1 mark]

4.8 The student wants to present her results as a graph.
Suggest a suitable type of graph she could use. Justify your choice.

....

....

....

[2 marks]

Turn over for the next question

5   A skydiver jumps from an aeroplane and his motion is recorded.
Figure 7 shows the velocity-time graph of his fall.

Figure 7

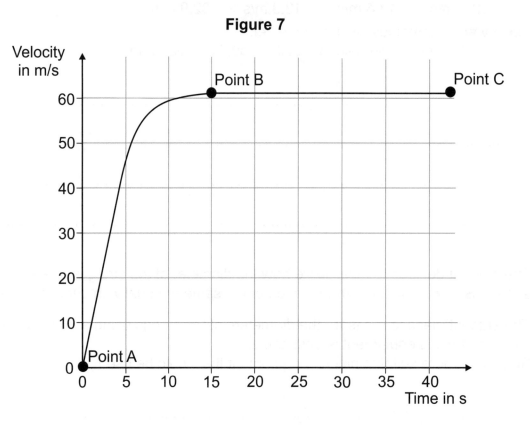

5.1   In the absence of air resistance, all objects accelerate towards the ground
at the same rate. State the magnitude of this acceleration.

....

[1 mark]

5.2   Points A, B and C are labelled on **Figure 7**.
Draw **one** line from each part of the skydiver's fall to the correct description of his
motion at this time.

	The skydiver has a positive acceleration
Between Point A and Point B	
	The skydiver is decelerating
Between Point B and Point C	
	The skydiver is moving at a constant velocity

[2 marks]

5.3   After 15 seconds the skydiver reaches his terminal velocity.
Name the contact force acting on the skydiver at this time.

....

[1 mark]

5.4   Write down the equation that links weight, mass and the gravitational field strength.

....

[1 mark]

5.5   The skydiver has a mass of 80.0 kg. Calculate his weight.
Use gravitational field strength = 9.8 N/kg.

....

....

Weight = ... N

[2 marks]

5.6   Once the skydiver has jumped, the plane accelerates away.
Write down the equation which links force, mass and acceleration.

....

[1 mark]

5.7   The plane experiences a resultant driving force of 58 500 N as it accelerates.
The plane has a mass of 4680 kg.
Calculate the acceleration of the plane.

....

....

....

Acceleration = ... m/s²

[3 marks]

Turn over for the next question

6   **Table 3** shows data from the Highway Code about stopping distances for a well-maintained car travelling on dry roads at various speeds.

Table 3

Speed (km/h)	Thinking distance (m)	Braking distance (m)	Stopping distance (m)
32	6	6	12
64	12		36
96	18	55	73

6.1   Complete **Table 3** by calculating the missing braking distance.

[1 mark]

6.2   The data in **Table 3** was obtained by observing a large number of drivers and calculating average distances. Explain why a large sample of people was used.

....

....

....

[2 marks]

6.3   A car is travelling down a road. A hazard appears ahead.
Which of the following factors will the thinking distance of the car depend on?
Tick **two** boxes.

☐   Whether the driver is tired.

☐   Whether the road is wet.

☐   How worn the tyres are.

☐   The speed the car is travelling at.

☐   The mass of the car.

[2 marks]

75 000 J of work must be done to stop the car. The braking force of the car is 5000 N.

6.4   Write down the equation that links distance, force and work done.

....

[1 mark]

6.5   Calculate the braking distance of the car.

....

....

Distance = ... m

[3 marks]

7 A student passes a current through a straight wire.
The current is flowing into the paper.

7.1 Which of the following shows the magnetic field around the wire?
Tick **one** box.

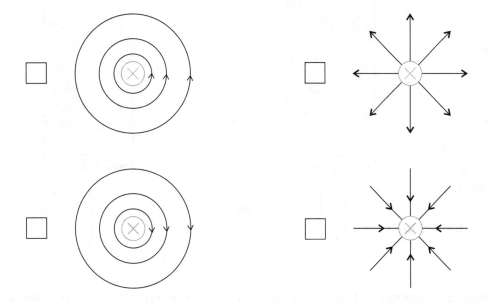

[1 mark]

7.2 A bar magnet is placed near the wire and experiences a force.
State **two** ways that the force on the magnet could be decreased
without removing it from the wire's magnetic field completely.

1. ....

....

2. ....

....

[2 marks]

Question 7 continues on the next page

7.3 The student coils the wire and inserts an iron core to form an electromagnet.
Figure 8 shows a bar magnet and an iron nail hanging from the electromagnet.

Figure 8

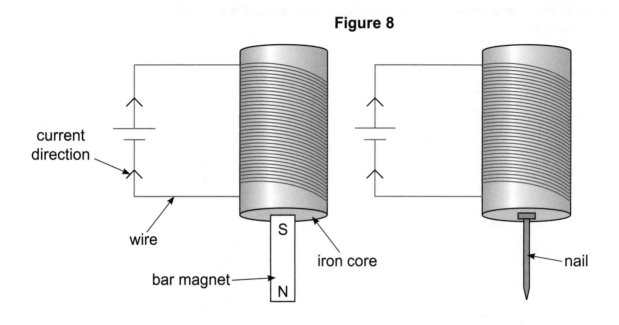

Predict what will happen to the bar magnet and the nail when the electromagnet is disconnected from the battery in each case. Justify your answer.

....

....

....

....

....

....

....

....

....

....

....

[6 marks]

END OF QUESTIONS

Answers

Topic 1 – Energy

Page 26-27
Warm-Up Questions
1) Any two from: mechanically (by a force doing work) / electrically (work done by when a current flows) / by heating / by radiation.
2) Energy is transferred (mechanically) from the chemical energy store of the person's arm to the kinetic energy stores of the arm and the ball.
3) True
4) A lorry travelling at 60 miles per hour.
5) Energy can be transferred usefully, stored or dissipated, but can never be created or destroyed.

Exam Questions
1   The thermal energy store of the metal block *[1 mark]*
2

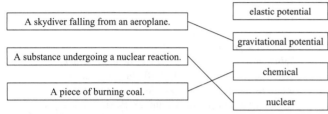

[3 marks for all correct, otherwise 2 marks for 2 correct or 1 mark for 1 correct]

3.1 The elastic potential energy store of the spring *[1 mark]*
3.2 kinetic energy = ½ × mass × speed² / $E_k = \frac{1}{2}mv^2$ *[1 mark]*
Allow velocity instead of speed in the relationship.
3.3 $E_k = \frac{1}{2} \times 0.20 \times 0.9^2$ *[1 mark]*
   = **0.081 J** *[1 mark]*
4.1 gravitational potential energy = mass × gravitational field strength × height / $E_p = mgh$ *[1 mark]*
4.2 Rearrange $E_p = mgh$ for h:
   $h = E_p \div (m \times g)$ *[1 mark]*
   = 137.2 ÷ (20 × 9.8) *[1 mark]*
   = **0.7 m** *[1 mark]*
4.3 Energy is transferred from the gravitational potential energy store *[1 mark]* to the kinetic energy store of the load *[1 mark]*.
4.4 Some of the energy would also be transferred to thermal energy store of the air (and the thermal energy store of the load) *[1 mark]*.
5   change in thermal energy = mass × specific heat capacity × temperature change / $\Delta E = mc\Delta\theta$
   So, $c = \Delta E \div (m \times \Delta\theta)$ *[1 mark]*
   c = 36 000 ÷ (0.5 × 80) *[1 mark]*
   = **900 J/kg °C** *[1 mark]*

Page 31
Warm-Up Questions
1) Power is the rate of energy transfer/doing work.
2) 1 J/s
3) E.g. its thickness/thermal conductivity
4) A material with a high thermal conductivity.
5) Some energy is always dissipated, so less than 100% of the input energy transfer is transferred usefully.

Exam Questions
1.1 power = work done ÷ time / $P = W \div t$ *[1 mark]*
1.2 1 kJ = 1000 J
   P = 1000 ÷ 20 *[1 mark]*
   = **50 W** *[1 mark]*
1.3 E.g. by lubricating any moving parts *[1 mark]*
1.4 It will be faster. *[1 mark]*
The motor transfers the same amount of energy, but over a shorter time.
2.1 Any one from: e.g. by heating the fan / by heating the surroundings / transferred away by sound waves *[1 mark]*.
2.2 2 kJ = 2 × 1000 = 2000 J *[1 mark]*
   useful output energy transfer
   = total input energy transfer – wasted output energy transfer
   = 7250 – 2000
   = **5250 J** *[1 mark]*
2.3 efficiency = $\dfrac{\text{useful output energy transfer}}{\text{total input energy transfer}}$
   = $\dfrac{5250}{7250}$ *[1 mark]*
   = 0.72413... = **0.72 (to 2 s.f.)** *[1 mark]*

Page 39
Warm-Up Questions
1) Any two from: coal / oil / natural gas.
2) Fossil fuels can be used to generate electricity at any time, but solar power cannot be used at night and is not reliable in cloudy weather.
3) Any one from: e.g. bio-fuels can be used to run vehicles / electricity generated using renewable resources can be used to power vehicles.
4) Any two from: e.g. it releases greenhouse gases and contributes to global warming / it causes acid rain / coal mining damages the landscape.
5) True

Exam Questions
1   wind *[1 mark]*
2   They can produce sulfur dioxide and cause acid rain. *[1 mark]*
3.1 E.g. Heating *[1 mark]*.
3.2 Any two from: e.g. it's expensive to build new renewable power plants / people don't want to live near new power stations / some renewable energy resources aren't very reliable, so they could not be used on their own / it's expensive to switch to cars running on renewable energy *[1 mark for each correct answer]*
4.1 How to grade your answer:
   Level 0: There is no relevant information. *[No marks]*
   Level 1: Some points are made about the environmental impact and reliability of wind power and hydro-electric power, but the energy resources are not directly compared. Answer lacks detail and structure. *[1 to 2 marks]*
   Level 2: At least three valid comparisons are made about the environmental impact and the reliability of wind power and hydro-electric power. Answer has some detail and structure. *[3 to 4 marks]*
   Level 3: At least four valid comparisons are made about the environmental impact and the reliability of wind power and hydro-electric power. Answer is detailed and well-structured. *[5 to 6 marks]*
   Here are some points your answer may include:
   Wind turbines do not do any permanent damage to the landscape.
   Building a hydro-electric power plant does damage the landscape, as it involves flooding a valley.

Hydro-electric power stations have a larger impact on the local environment than wind turbines since animals and plants in the flooded valley lose their habitats.
Wind turbines and hydro-electric power stations produce no pollution once they are built.
However, plants in valleys flooded for hydro-electric power stations can rot, producing greenhouse gases which lead to global warming.
Hydro-electric power is reliable in countries that have regular rainfall, but wind turbines are unable to produce electricity when wind stops or when the wind is too strong.
Hydro-electric power stations can respond straight away when there is additional demand, but the power supplied by wind turbines cannot be increased.

4.2   E.g. they cause no pollution *[1 mark]*

Topic 2 — Electricity

Page 47
Warm-Up Questions

1)

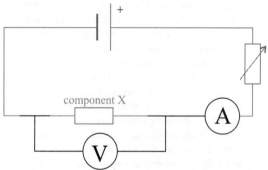

2)   Electric current is a flow of electric charge.
3)   Ohms / Ω
4)   Any one from: e.g. a wire / a fixed resistor
5)   In parallel.
6)   A graph that shows how the current flowing through a component changes as the potential difference across it varies.

Exam Questions

1.1 $Q = It$ / charge flow = current × time *[1 mark]*.
1.2   Convert from minutes into seconds:
       2 minutes = 120 seconds
       $Q = It$
          = 0.30 × 120
          = **36 C**
       [2 marks for correct answer, otherwise 1 mark for correctly converting from minutes to seconds]
1.3   A filament lamp is a **non-linear** *[1 mark]* component. As the temperature of the filament increases, the **resistance** *[1 mark]* of the lamp increases.

2.1

[1 mark for adding the ammeter in line with component X, 1 mark for adding the voltmeter across component X]

2.2   A straight line *[1 mark]*. Component X is a resistor, which is an ohmic/linear component *[1 mark]*.

Page 55
Warm-Up Questions

1)   Any one from: e.g. in automatic night lights / outdoor lighting / burglar detectors.
2)   The resistance decreases.
3)   The components are all connected in a line between the ends of the power supply.
4)   True
5)   The total resistance is the sum of all the resistances.
6)   Two resistors connected in series.

Exam Questions

1   Total resistance is equal to the sum of the individual resistances. *[1 mark]*
2.1 $R_{total} = R_1 + R_2$
          = 3 + 2 *[1 mark]* = **5 Ω** *[1 mark]*
2.2   0.4 A *[1 mark]*. Current is the same throughout a series circuit *[1 mark]*.
2.3 $V_{total} = V_1 + V_2$
       $V_2 = V_{total} - V_1$
          = 4.0 − 1.6 *[1 mark]*
          = **2.4 V** *[1 mark]*
3.1   When current flows, the LED will be lit. *[1 mark]*
3.2   When the lights are switched off, the resistance of the LDR increases *[1 mark]*. As a result the total resistance of the circuit also increases, since it is equal to the sum of the individual resistances *[1 mark]*.

Page 61
Warm-Up Questions

1)   The live wire, neutral wire, and earth wire.
2)   Energy is transferred electrically to the thermal energy store of the heating element.
3)   power = (current)^2 × resistance / $P = I^2 R$
4)   The network of cables and transformers that distributes electricity across the country.

Exam Questions

1.1   **Step-up** *[1 mark]* transformers are used between the power station and the transmission cables. This increases the **potential difference** *[1 mark]*, so that power may be transferred more efficiently.
1.2   230 V ac *[1 mark]*
2.1 $P = VI$ / power = potential difference × current *[1 mark]*
2.2 $P = VI$
       $I = \dfrac{P}{V}$
          $= \dfrac{2760}{230}$ *[1 mark]*
          = **12 A** *[1 mark]*
2.3   E.g. volume of water / starting temperature *[1 mark]*
2.4   Energy transferred = power × time / Power is the rate of energy transfer *[1 mark]*. So kettle B will transfer more energy in the same time *[1 mark]*.

Topic 3 — Particle Model of Matter

Pages 69-70
Warm-Up Questions

1)   In a solid, the particles are close together and are held in a regular, fixed pattern.
2)   A measure of how much mass there is in a certain space.
3)   It increases.
4)   The specific latent heat of vaporisation of a substance is the amount of energy needed to change 1 kg of that substance from a liquid to a gas.
5)   J/kg

Exam Questions

1   If a liquid is heated to a certain temperature it starts to boil and turns into a **gas** *[1 mark]*. Another process that causes this change of state is **evaporation** *[1 mark]*.

2.1   The densities of each of the toy soldiers are the same, but their masses may vary. *[1 mark]*

2.2   200 g = 0.2 kg
density = mass ÷ volume = $0.2 ÷ (2.5 \times 10^{-5})$ *[1 mark]*
= **8000 kg/m³** *[1 mark]*

3   $E = mL = 0.40 \times 1200$ *[1 mark]*
= **480 J** *[1 mark]*

4.1   The volume of the pendant *[1 mark]*.
The mass of the pendant *[1 mark]*.

4.2   E.g. measure the mass of the pendant using the mass balance *[1 mark]*. Fill the eureka can with water to just below the spout, then place the measuring cylinder beneath the spout *[1 mark]*. To measure the volume of the pendant, submerge the pendant in the water, catching the displaced water in the measuring cylinder *[1 mark]*. Measure the volume of the displaced water, which is equal to the volume of the pendant *[1 mark]*. Divide the mass of the pendant by the volume of the pendant to find the density *[1 mark]*.

With questions where you have to describe a method, make sure your description is clear and detailed. You could also pick up some of the marks by describing how you'd do repeats, take averages and other ways in which you'd make it a fair test.

5.1   The substance is melting *[1 mark]*.

5.2   Melting point = −7 °C *[1 mark]*
Boiling point = 58 °C *[1 mark]*

6   How to grade your answer:
Level 0:   There is no relevant information. *[No marks]*
Level 1:   There is a brief explanation of what happens to the particles in the gas as the container is heated. *[1 to 2 marks]*
Level 2:   An attempt is made to use the particle model to explain how gas particles create pressure in a sealed container. This is linked to a brief explanation of why the pressure of the gas increases as the container is heated. *[3 to 4 marks]*
Level 3:   The particle model is used to provide a clear explanation of how gas particles create pressure in a sealed container. This is used to give a detailed explanation of why the pressure of the gas increases. *[5 to 6 marks]*

Here are some points your answer may include:
In a sealed container, the gas particles are free to move around.
The particles collide with the walls of the container.
Each collision exerts a force on the walls.
The overall force creates an outward pressure.
When the container is heated, energy is transferred to the particles' kinetic energy stores.
This means that the particles move faster.
Since the particles are moving faster, they collide with the container walls more often.
So the force exerted on the container walls, and therefore the pressure, increases as the container is heated.

Topic 4 — Atomic Structure

Page 82-83
Warm-Up Questions

1)   Evidence from alpha particle scattering experiments showed that the plum pudding model could not be correct. The evidence suggested that atoms were mostly empty space, and that most of the mass was in the centre of the atom as a small, positive nucleus.

2)   An atom contains a tiny, positively charged, nucleus made up of protons and neutrons. The nucleus is surrounded by electrons, which orbit the nucleus in energy levels.

3)   Electromagnetic radiation.

4)   A positive ion.
Atoms are neutral overall. If an atom loses an electron, it has more positive protons than negative electrons. So it now has a positive charge.

5)   The mass number tells you the total number of protons and neutrons.

6)   Alpha decay: mass number decreases by 4 and the atomic number decreases by 2.
Gamma decay: the mass and atomic numbers don't change.

7)   Contamination occurs when radioactive atoms get onto or inside an object. Irradiation occurs is when radiation from a radioactive sources reaches an object.

8)   Gamma radiation is less ionising than alpha or beta radiation, so it does the least harm as it passes through the body.

Exam Questions

1.1   Protons *[1 mark]*, neutrons *[1 mark]*

1.2   Atoms with the same atomic number but a different mass number *[1 mark]*.

2

Particle	Charge	Number present in an atom of iodine-131
Proton	positive	53
Neutron	zero	78
Electron	negative	53

[1 mark for each correct answer]

The bottom number in $^{131}_{53}$I is the atomic number, which is the number of protons. The top number is the total number of protons and neutrons. So there are 131 − 53 = 78 neutrons.

3

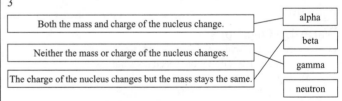

[1 mark for each correct line]

4.1   Beta (particles) *[1 mark]*, because the radiation passes through the paper, but not the aluminium *[1 mark]*.

4.2   E.g. a Geiger-Muller tube (and counter) *[1 mark]*

5.1   28 minutes *[1 mark]*
The initial activity is 740 Bq. Half of this is 740 ÷ 2 = 370 Bq. The activity falls to this level between 20 and 30 minutes, so from the options, 28 minutes must be the half-life.

5.2   Irradiation from the source isn't much of a concern because alpha radiation only travels a few centimetres in air and cannot get through the skin to damage organs *[1 mark]*. However, if the student's hands are contaminated by atoms of the radioactive source, they could end up inside her body, where the alpha radiation would do a lot of damage as it is highly ionising *[1 mark]*.

Topic 5 — Forces

Page 88
Warm-Up Questions
1) friction
2) the magnitude of the vector
3) a) kg
   b) N
4) Add the forces together.

Exam Questions
1.1 force *[1 mark]*
1.2 14 kg *[1 mark]*
2.1 $800 - (300 + 200) = $ **300 N** *[1 mark]* **down** *[1 mark]*
2.2 $x - 400 = 0 \Rightarrow x =$ **400 N** *[1 mark]*
3.1 Work done = force × distance / $W = Fs$ *[1 mark]*
3.2 $W = 44\,000 \times 750$ *[1 mark]*
   $= 33\,000\,000$ J *[1 mark]*
   $= $ **33 000 kJ** *[1 mark]*

Remember, to convert from J to kJ, divide by 1000.

Page 93
Warm-Up Questions
1) true
2) false
3) metres

Exam Questions
1.1 $F = ke$ / Force = spring constant × extension *[1 mark]*
1.2 $k = F \div e$ *[1 mark]*
   $= 4 \div 0.05$ *[1 mark]*
   $= $ **80 N/m** *[1 mark]*
2.1 E.g. the spring used (so the spring constant remains
   the same) *[1 mark]*
2.2 E.g. the mass attached to the spring / the force applied to the
   spring *[1 mark]*
2.3 Extension = 4.0 cm = 0.040 m
   Work done = $^1/_2 \times 175 \times 0.040^2$ *[1 mark]*
   $= $ **0.14** *[1 mark]* **J** *[1 mark]*

You can read the extension from the graph. Don't forget to convert it to m.

Page 99
Warm-Up Questions
1) Speed is a scalar, velocity is a vector /
   velocity has a direction, speed does not.
2) a) E.g. 3 m/s
   b) E.g. 30 m/s
   c) E.g. 250 m/s
*Your answers may be slightly different to these, but as long as they're about
the same size, you should be fine to use them in the exam.*
3) true
4) a flat section.
5) 0 N.

Exam Questions
1 acceleration = $(10 - 2.0) \div 20$ *[1 mark]*
   $= $ **0.4 m/s²** *[1 mark]*
2.1 The cyclist travels at a constant speed (of 3 m/s) between
   5 s and 8 s *[1 mark]*, then decelerates (with decreasing
   deceleration) between 8 s and 10 s *[1 mark]*.
2.2 Acceleration is given by the gradient of a velocity-time graph.
   change in $y = 3 - 0 = 3$ m/s
   change in $x = 5 - 2 = 3$ s
   acceleration = $3 \div 3$ *[1 mark]* $= $ **1 m/s²** *[1 mark]*
3.1 Distance = speed × time / $s = vt$ *[1 mark]*

3.2 Distance rolled = 0.46×2.4 *[1 mark]*
   $= 1.104$ *[1 mark]*
   $= $ **1.1 m (to 2 s.f.)** *[1 mark]*
3.3 $v^2 - u^2 = 2as$
   $a = \dfrac{v^2 - u^2}{2s}$ *[1 mark]*
   $= \dfrac{12^2 - 0^2}{2 \times 8}$ *[1 mark]*
   $= $ **9 m/s²** *[1 mark]*

Page 104
Warm-Up Questions
1) true
2) Boulder B
*Boulder B needs a greater force to accelerate it by the same amount as
boulder A.*
3) true
This is Newton's Third Law.

Exam Questions
1.1 The ball exerts a force of –520 N on the bat *[1 mark]*.
1.2 The acceleration of the ball will be **greater than** that of the
   bat because it has a smaller mass. *[1 mark]*
1.3 Force = mass × acceleration
   acceleration = force ÷ mass *[1 mark]*
   $= 520 \div 1.6$ *[1 mark]*
   $= $ **325 m/s²** *[1 mark]*
2.1 0 N *[1 mark]*
*The van is travelling at a constant speed in one
direction so the resultant force must be zero.*
2.2 The driving force decreases *[1 mark]*
   The wind blowing in the opposite direction to
   the van's movement increases *[1 mark]*
2.3 $F = ma$
   $= 2500 \times 1.4$ *[1 mark]*
   $= $ **3500 N** *[1 mark]*
   opposite to the direction of motion *[1 mark]*

Page 108
Warm-Up Questions
1) reaction time / speed / tiredness / drugs / alcohol.
2) The braking distance.
3) Large decelerations may lead to brakes
   overheating/the car skidding.
4) true

Exam Questions
1.1 Thinking distance *[1 mark]*.
1.2 The distance the car travels during its deceleration whilst the
   brakes are being applied *[1 mark]*.
2.1 It reduces the frictional force of the tyres on the road, which
   increases the braking distance *[1 mark]*.
2.2 E.g. decrease their speed *[1 mark]*.
2.3 Energy transferred from:
   The car's kinetic energy stores *[1 mark]*
   Energy transferred to:
   The brakes' thermal energy stores *[1 mark]*
3.1 Average reaction time = $(0.24 + 0.19 + 0.23) \div 3$ *[1 mark]*
   $= 0.22$ s *[1 mark]*
3.2 E.g. use the same ruler in each test / add a ball of
   modelling clay to the bottom of the ruler to help
   it fall straight down each time / repeat the test
   more times and take an average *[1 mark]*.

Topic 6 – Waves

Page 116
Warm-Up Questions
1) E.g. If an object is dropped into calm water, ripples spread out. The ripples don't carry the water or the object away with them though. / If a guitar string is strummed, the sound waves don't carry the air away from the guitar. If they did, a wind would be created.
2) In a longitudinal wave, the vibrations are parallel to the direction of travel/energy transfer.
3) rarefactions
4) true

Exam Questions
1.1 E.g. The particles vibrate at right angles to the direction of energy transfer *[1 mark]*
1.2 5 cm *[1 mark]*
1.3 2 m *[1 mark]*
2.1 The wavelength of the sound waves *[1 mark]*.
2.2 wave speed = frequency × wavelength / $v = f\lambda$ *[1 mark]*
2.3 $v = f\lambda$
   $= 50.0 \times 6.8$ *[1 mark]*
   $= \mathbf{340}$ *[1 mark]* **m/s** *[1 mark]*

Page 123-124
Warm-Up Questions
1) gamma rays
2) 7
3) Gamma rays are created by changes in the nucleus of an atom.
4) E.g. Infrared cameras / heating / cooking
5) Any two from: e.g. sunburn / the skin can age prematurely / the risk of skin cancer is increased.

Exam Questions
1 visible light *[1 mark]*
2.1 X-rays *[1 mark]*
2.2 E.g. Exposure could cause cancer / cell mutations / damage cells *[1 mark]*.
3.1 low-frequency infrared *[1 mark]*
3.2 They don't travel faster than radio signals because all electromagnetic waves travel at the same speed in a vacuum *[1 mark]*.
4.1 Any one from: e.g. time temperature increase is measured over / type/size of beaker / the amount of water in each beaker / the size/thickness of each piece of card / the distance of each thermometer from the beaker / the height of each thermometer *[1 mark]*
4.2 Any one from: e.g. be careful when pouring/ carrying hot water / don't touch the beakers until they have cooled down *[1 mark]*.
4.3 29 °C *[1 mark]*
4.4 More infrared radiation is emitted from matt surfaces than from shiny surfaces *[1 mark]*.
4.5 Any one from: e.g. repeat the experiment and calculate averages / use infrared detectors instead of thermometers *[1 mark]*.

Topic 7 — Magnetism and Electromagnetism

Page 130
Warm-Up Questions
1)

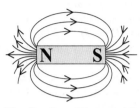

2) The direction of the magnetic field.
3) By wrapping it into a spring-shaped coil.

Exam Questions
1.1

[1 mark for arrows on all lines pointing north to south].
1.2 Attraction *[1 mark]* — opposite poles attract *[1 mark]*.
2 Cobalt is an example of a **magnetic material** *[1 mark]*. The force between a piece of cobalt and a bar magnet is always **attractive** *[1 mark]*.
3.1 Concentric circles around the wire / circles centred on the wire *[1 mark]*. The field will be in a clockwise direction around the wire *[1 mark]*.

If you need to state the direction of a circular field, it's usually easiest to describe the field as either going clockwise or anticlockwise.

3.2 The field lines of the loops line up *[1 mark]*. The field lines are now closer, meaning the magnetic field is stronger *[1 mark]*.

Practice Paper 1

1.1 liquid *[1 mark]*
1.2 potential energy *[1 mark]*, kinetic energy *[1 mark]*
1.3 gas *[1 mark]*

There are two flat bits on the graph that show changes of state. The first must show the substance melting and the second must show it boiling. So at Z it must be a gas.

1.4 X *[1 mark]*
1.5 The specific latent heat of fusion of the substance is 334 000 J/kg. *[1 mark]*
1.6 $E = mL = 5.00 \times 334\,000$ *[1 mark]*
   $= \mathbf{1\,670\,000\ J}$ *[1 mark]*
2.1 Volume = length × width × height
   $= 4.0 \times 4.0 \times 4.0$ *[1 mark]*
   $= \mathbf{64\ cm^3}$ *[1 mark]*
2.2 He should use cylinder A. The graduations are smaller on cylinder A, so the student will be able to make more accurate measurements *[1 mark]*.
2.3 density $= 0.435 \div 0.000058$ *[1 mark]*
   $= \mathbf{7500\ kg/m^3}$ *[1 mark]*
3.1 The type of insulation *[1 mark]*.
3.2 Any two from, e.g. thickness of insulation / starting temperature of the water / length of time water is left to cool / volume of water used / the beaker used / temperature of the room *[1 mark for each]*
3.3 Mean temperature = $(21.9 + 22.2 + 20.1) \div 3$ *[1 mark]*
   $= \mathbf{21.4\ °C}$ *[1 mark]*

3.4   E.g. the insulation does not cover the top of the beaker *[1 mark]*. This means a lot of energy is being lost from the top of the beaker *[1 mark]*. The amount of energy lost through the insulation is small in comparison, meaning that the decrease in energy is roughly the same each time *[1 mark]*.

3.5   With a thick layer of material that has a low thermal conductivity. *[1 mark]*

3.6   E.g. biofuel / waves / hydroelectricity / the tides *[1 mark]*

3.7   In 10 years she would save £375 × 10 = £3750 on her energy bill *[1 mark]*. This would not cover the £6000 cost of installing the solar panels, so the home owner would not save money *[1 mark]*.

4.1   It is twice as large as the resistance of circuit A. *[1 mark]*

4.2   E.g. The current is higher in circuit A *[1 mark]*. When potential difference is the same, the greater the resistance in the circuit, the smaller the current. Potential difference is the same in both circuits so the current in circuit A is higher because its resistance is lower *[1 mark]*.

4.3   The potential difference across each resistor is 6 V. *[1 mark]*

4.4   power = 3.0^2 × 4.0 *[1 mark]* = **36** *[1 mark]* **watts** *[1 mark]*

4.5   The resistance decreases *[1 mark]*.

4.6   E.g. a car engine temperature sensor / an electronic thermostat *[1 mark]*.

4.7

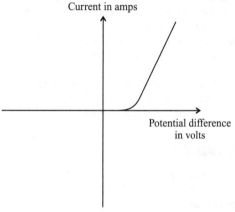

[1 mark for zero current at negative potential differences, 1 mark for curve into positive-gradient at a non-zero positive potential difference]

5.1   How to grade your answer:

Level 0:   There is no relevant information. *[No marks]*

Level 1:   There is a brief description of how to calculate the resistance of different lengths of wire. The answer is missing key details. *[1 to 2 marks]*

Level 2:   There is a brief summary of the experimental procedure, including one way to ensure accurate results. The answer states which quantities need to be measured and explains how they can be used to calculate the resistance of the wire. *[3 to 4 marks]*

Level 3:   There is full, clear and logical description of the experimental procedure. The answer states which quantities need to be measured and how they can be used to calculate the resistance of the wire. At least two ways to ensure the results of the experiment will be accurate are given. *[5 to 6 marks]*

Here are some points your answer may include:

Procedure

Attach a crocodile clip to the wire level with 0 cm on the ruler.
Attach the second crocodile clip to the wire, e.g. 5 cm from the first clip.
Write down the length of the wire between the clips.
Close the switch, then record the current through the wire and the potential across it.

Rearrange $V = IR$ to $R = V \div I$ and use this equation to calculate the resistance of the wire.
Repeat the procedure several times, moving the second crocodile clip further along each time to create a longer wire, e.g. move it 5 cm along each time to create wires of lengths 10 cm, 15 cm, 20 cm and 25 cm.
Plot a graph of resistance against wire length to see the relationship between the two.

Improving accuracy

If the wires heat up their resistance will increase, making the results less accurate.
To reduce the heating effect:
1. Switch off the circuit between measurements to allow the circuit to cool down / stop the circuit heating up.
2. Use a battery with a low potential difference / only use low currents (as the larger the current, the more the circuit will heat up).
Repeat all wire length measurements to ensure the correct length is measured. Draw lines on the crocodile clips as distance markers, to ensure the distance is being measured between the same points each time.
Tape the wire down onto the ruler to ensure the wire is straight and there are no kinks.
Ensure that the length measurements are taken at eye level to avoid errors due to parallax.
Make sure the same part of the crocodile clip is in contact with the wire each time it is moved or the resistance of the crocodile clip may affect the results.
Repeat the measurements of potential difference and current several times for each length of wire and use them to calculate a mean resistance for each length of wire.
This will minimise the amount of random error in the results and allow anomalous results to be easily identified.

5.2

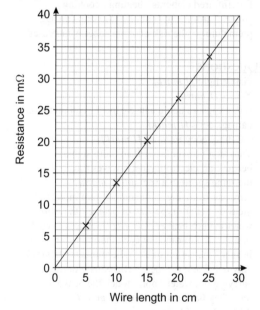

[1 mark for points correctly plotted, 1 mark for sensible line of best fit]

5.3   40 mΩ *[1 mark for value between 39 and 41 mΩ]*

5.4   As the length of the wire increases, its resistance increases *[1 mark]*.

6.1   **W** and **Y** *[1 mark]*

6.2   **X** *[1 mark]*

6.3   Gravitational potential energy = mass × gravitational field strength × height / GPE = $m \times g \times h$ *[1 mark]*

6.4   mass = 1 500 000 g = 1500 kg
Gravitational P.E. = 1500 × 9.8 × 40.0 *[1 mark]*
        = **588 000 J** *[1 mark]*

6.5   elastic potential energy store (of the spring) *[1 mark]*

6.6   efficiency = $\dfrac{\text{useful energy output}}{\text{total energy output}}$ *[1 mark]*

6.7   efficiency = $\dfrac{18.0}{59.5}$ *[1 mark]*

        = 0.3025... = **0.303 (to 3 s.f.)** *[1 mark]*

You could also have given the efficiency as a percentage.
To get a percentage, multiply by 100: 0.303 × 100 = 30.3%

6.8   Lubricating the moving parts of the carriage will decrease the energy lost due to frictional forces *[1 mark]*. This means more energy will be transferred to the kinetic energy store of the carriage *[1 mark]*. Kinetic energy = ½mv^2, so the velocity/speed will increase *[1 mark]*.

7.1   214 − 83 = **131 neutrons** *[1 mark]*

7.2   Because they have the same number of protons/are the same element *[1 mark]* and have a different number of neutrons/have a different mass number *[1 mark]*.

7.3

$^{222}_{86}\text{Rn}$ *[1 mark]*

$^{210}_{83}\text{Bi}$ *[1 mark]*

7.4   420 days *[1 mark]*

7.5   Half-life when activity drops to half original total.
Activity after 1 half-life = 80 ÷ 2 = 40 Bq
Using **Figure 14**, when activity = 40 Bq, time = 140 days.
Therefore, half-life =**140 days** *[1 mark]*

7.6   Contamination is when unwanted radioactive atoms are on or inside an object *[1 mark]*.

7.7   How to grade your answer:
      Level 0:   There is no relevant information. *[No marks]*
      Level 1:   There is a brief explanation on the dangers of alpha and beta contamination, but little to no comparison between them. The answer has little or no clear structure. *[1 to 2 marks]*
      Level 2:   There is a clear explanation and comparison of the dangers of alpha and beta contamination both inside and outside the body. The answer is well structured. *[3 to 4 marks]*
      Here are some points your answer may include:
      Inside the body, the release of alpha particles is more dangerous than the release of beta particles.
      This is because alpha particles are more ionising than beta particles, so they can cause more damage to cells.
      Outside the body, the release of beta particles is more dangerous than the release of alpha particles.
      This is because alpha particles are easily absorbed by thin barriers, so it is unlikely to pass through the skin if the contaminating atoms are outside the body.
      But beta particles from contaminating atoms outside the body can pass through skin and damage internal organs.

Practice Paper 2

1.1   1 N *[1 mark]*

The spring is still, so the forces acting on it must be balanced.

1.2   If only one force was applied this would simply cause the spring to move in the direction of the force. *[1 mark]*

1.3   random error *[1 mark]*

Using a marker ensures that you're always measuring the length of the spring from the same point.

1.4   E.g. 6.0 N (allow estimate from 5.5 N up to 6.5 N) *[1 mark]*. The graph is a straight line up to that point which shows extension and force are proportional *[1 mark]*.

1.5   0.015 m = 1.5 cm
From the graph a force of 3.0 N causes this extension.
[1 mark for evidence of conversion to 1.5 cm. 1 mark for correct force.]

1.6   spring constant = 3.0 ÷ 0.015 *[1 mark]* = **200 N/m** *[1 mark]*

2.1   0 N *[1 mark]*

When an object is travelling at a constant speed in a fixed direction it is not accelerating and so the resultant force will be zero.

2.2   Speed is the gradient of a distance-time graph.
change in vertical axis = 20 − 11= 9 m
change in horizontal axis = 27 − 15 = 12 s
speed = 9 ÷ 12 *[1 mark]* = **0.75 m/s** *[1 mark]*

2.3   Between 9 metres and 10 metres *[1 mark]*.

The swimmer is travelling fastest when the gradient of the graph is steepest.

2.4   speed = 20 ÷ 23 = 0.8695... m/s *[1 mark]*
        = **0.87 m/s (to 2 s.f.)** *[1 mark]*

2.5

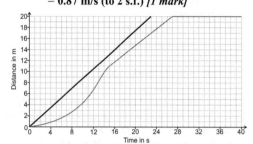

[1 mark for straight line, 1 mark for correct start and end points]

2.6   The magnitude of the swimmer's displacement is 0 m. *[1 mark]*

3.1   amplitude = 5 squares tall, one square = 1 cm tall
amplitude = 5 × 1 = **5 cm** *[1 mark]*

3.2   The number of complete waves that pass a point each second. *[1 mark]*

3.3   E.g. heating/cooking/infrared cameras *[1 mark]*

3.4   Variable 1 — Control *[1 mark]*
Variable 2 — Independent *[1 mark]*

3.5   The hypothesis is not supported as the white woollen blanket is not dark-coloured but has absorbed the signal *[1 mark]*.

3.6   How to grade your answer:
      Level 0:   There is no relevant information. *[No marks]*
      Level 1:   There is a clear description of at least one similarity and one difference between the features and properties of infrared waves and radio waves. *[1 to 2 marks]*
      Level 2:   There is a clear description of multiple similarities and differences between the features and properties of infrared waves and radio waves. *[3 to 4 marks]*
      Here are some points your answer may include:
      Both infrared and radio waves are electromagnetic waves.
      They are both transverse waves.
      The vibrations in both types of wave are perpendicular to the direction of energy transfer.
      Both types of wave travel at the same speed through air or a vacuum.
      Radio waves have a longer wavelength than infrared waves.
      Radio waves have a lower frequency than infrared waves.

4.1   E.g. wear goggles in case string snaps / remain standing so that they can get out of the way of any falling masses. *[1 mark]*

4.2   11.0 cm *[1 mark]*

Each half-wave is 27.5 ÷ 5 = 5.5 cm. So one full wave is 5.5 × 2 = 11.0 cm.

4.3   wave speed = frequency × wavelength / $v = f × λ$ *[1 mark]*

4.4   wavelength = 11.0 cm = 0.110 m
wave speed = 120 × 0.110 *[1 mark]*
        = **13.2 m/s** or 13 m/s (to 2 s.f.) *[1 mark]*

4.5   32.9 m/s is anomalous *[1 mark]*. The student should try to identify a reason for the anomalous result *[1 mark]*. If it is found to be due to an error, it should be ignored and not included when calculating the mean *[1 mark]*.

4.6   It is not suitable as the resolution of a ruler is too low *[1 mark]*. A micrometer/Vernier callipers would be more suitable *[1 mark]*.

Micrometers and vernier callipers have a much higher resolution than rulers.

4.7   As diameter decreases, wave speed increases /
As diameter increases, wave speed decreases *[1 mark]*.

4.8   A scatter/line graph *[1 mark]*. Diameter and speed
are both continuous variables *[1 mark]*.

5.1   9.8 m/s² *[1 mark]*

5.2   Between Point A and Point B —
The skydiver has a positive acceleration *[1 mark]*
Between Point B and Point C —
The skydiver is moving at a constant velocity *[1 mark]*

5.3   Air resistance / friction / drag *[1 mark]*

5.4   weight = mass × gravitational field strength /
$W = mg$ *[1 mark]*

5.5 $W = 80.0 × 9.8$ *[1 mark]* = **784 N** *[1 mark]*

5.6   force = mass × acceleration / $F = ma$ *[1 mark]*

5.7 $a = F ÷ m$ *[1 mark]*
       = 58 500 ÷ 4680 *[1 mark]* = **12.5 m/s²** *[1 mark]*

6.1   36 – 12 = **24 m** *[1 mark]*

6.2   Reaction times vary from person to person *[1 mark]*.
A large sample will give a more accurate average *[1 mark]*.

6.3   Whether the driver is tired. *[1 mark]*
The speed the car is travelling at. *[1 mark]*

6.4   Work done = force × distance *[1 mark]*

6.5   Rearranging work done = force × distance for distance:
distance = work done ÷ force *[1 mark]*
       = 75 000 ÷ 5000 *[1 mark]* = **15 m** *[1 mark]*

7.1

          [1 mark]

You need to use the right-hand thumb rule for this.

7.2   Decrease the current *[1 mark]*.
Move the magnet further from the wire *[1 mark]*.

7.3   How to grade your answer:

    Level 0:   There is no relevant information. *[No marks]*

    Level 1:   Predictions of what will happen to the bar
                 magnet and nail are given and a brief reason is
                 given for at least one of the predictions.
                 [1 to 2 marks]

    Level 2:   Predictions of what will happen to the bar
                 magnet and nail are given. There is some
                 explanation for each prediction, or a detailed
                 account of one of them. *[3 to 4 marks]*

    Level 3:   Predictions of what will happen to the bar
                 magnet and nail are given. There is a clear
                 and detailed explanation for each prediction.
                 [5 to 6 marks]

    Here are some points your answer may include:
    The bar magnet will remain attached to the electromagnet.
    The bar magnet is a permanent magnet.
    When the current stops flowing in the wire, the wire has no
    magnetic field around it.
    With the bar magnet attached, the iron core remains an
    induced magnet, as it's in the bar magnet's magnetic field.
    Permanent magnets and induced magnets always attract each
    other.
    So the bar magnet will remain stuck to the iron core
    (assuming the magnetic force is greater than the weight of
    the magnet).
    The nail will fall off.
    The nail was an induced magnet as it was in the magnetic
    field of the electromagnet.
    When the current stops flowing, the electromagnet and the
    nail both lose their magnetism.
    This means there is no attractive force keeping them together,
    so the nail will fall off.

Index

Index

SCPAFS41